C000186407

GROWING OLDER, L

GROWING OLDER, LIVING LONGER

Revolutionary Breakthroughs in the Science of Ageing

Teresa Hunt

THE BODLEY HEAD
LONDON

A CIP catalogue record for this book is
available from the British Library.

ISBN 0–370–31036–5
0–370–31226–0 (Pbk)
© Teresa Hunt 1988

Printed in Great Britain for
The Bodley Head Ltd,
32 Bedford Square, London WC1B 3EL
by The Alden Press Ltd, Oxford

First published in 1988

This book is dedicated to my father and also to Stuart, without whom...

Acknowledgements

I should like to thank the following experts and friends for taking time out of their busy schedules to read the relevant chapters and pass on much needed advice and helpful comments: Professor Tom Kirkwood, National Institute for Medical Research; Professor Robin Willson, Brunel University, London; Dr Richard Green, Astra Neuroscience Research Unit, London; Dr John Cummings, Dunn Nutrition Unit, Cambridge; Professor Clyde Williams, Department of Physical Education and Sports Science, Loughborough University.

Special thanks to Eamonn Matthews who was with me in New York when this book was first proposed and whose advice since then has been invaluable.

Contents

CHAPTER ONE

Ageing Past and Present

'Every man desires to live long, but no man would be old.'
Jonathan Swift

Like Swift, all people desire long lives but dread the consequences of longevity. This distaste with which so many regard
old age is due to fear of the degeneration which ageing is
thought to bring with it. The daily reminders of increasing age
creep up on us slowly until they become impossible to ignore,
and the older we get the more difficult it is to be subjective
about these changes. In a vain bid to offset the ravages of old
age, mankind has searched for the key to immortal life.

No other problem was quite as important to the ancient
alchemists as the search for an elixir which would postpone old
age. According to legend, the sorceress Medea stumbled on the
secret. She took old King Aeson and bled him dry and then
filled his empty veins with a cocktail of grasses, roots and
herbs, the blood of a black ram, the flesh of an owl and the skin
of a snake. Revitalised after the 'blood' transfusion, he burst
out of bed overflowing with youth and vitality.

Inhalation of the breath of young girls was another
rejuvenatory favourite. King David slept with young virgins in
the hope of absorbing their revitalising exhalations. Abishag of
Shunau was brought to lie with the King in the hope that her
'breath' or 'heat' would rejuvenate him, but without much
success, for he 'knew her not' and died soon after. This
principle of Shunamitism went on to become quite popular in
the seventeenth and eighteenth centuries.

Hebrews and Syrians were not exempt from joining the
search and turned to drink; their favourite tipple was the blood

of young men. Romans apparently sucked blood mixed with milk from the breasts of young slave girls, although whether this reinforced 'pinta' made them live longer is not recorded. Blood was to remain a favourite elixir and the blood of children, even infants, was transferred into the veins of the old in the hope of rejuvenation. Pope Innocent VIII had transfusions from three young men to no avail. His Holiness had not heard about the need to match blood groups, and shortened his life in his quest for immortality.

Then in 1889, Charles Brown-Séquard, a 72-year-old distinguished French physiologist, injected himself with an extract of dogs' testicles and proclaimed to the doctors of Paris that he felt 30 years younger, reporting that 'the physiological effects of the extract will appear to you, as they appeared to me, most surprising. It is sufficient to state that everything I had not been able to do or had done badly for several years on account of my advanced age I am today able to perform most admirably.' According to Brown-Séquard the extract had cured his impotence and allowed him better control of his bladder.

However, the scientific community was not impressed. Brown-Séquard thought the rejuvenating factor in his testis extract was normally present in the seminal fluid which contains sperm. He was later proved correct in the assumption that the testis produces a secretion, the male sex hormone called testosterone. Where Brown-Séquard was wrong was to think that testosterone was not only the key to sexual vigour, but would open the door to the secrets of eternal youth. Although he was to leave research under a cloud of scientific ridicule, his early experiments could be thought of as the forerunner of the scientific study of hormones.

Brown-Séquard's successor, a Russian named Serge Veronoff, grafted monkeys' testicles onto elderly males with failing sexual powers. His fame spread quickly and within a few years he had built up a list of international patients. By the time of his death he was considered a quack and testicle transplants were the subject of great amusement.

He was operating at a time in scientific history when there was a great deal of ignorance about tissue transplantation. Claims were made for the success of grafts from an animal to a human, even though we know now that the body's immune system is designed to reject foreign tissue of any sort.

Eugen Steinach, an Austrian endocrinologist living in Vienna, offered rejuvenation by tying off the vas deferens, the tube through which the semen is transported. According to his theory, this rudimentary vasectomy, would push testosterone back into the bloodstream where it would rejuvenate the patient. So far, there has been no evidence that men who have undergone vasectomies have been rejuvenated. Steinach and Veronoff both had their moments of glory during which their respective 'rejuvenation' procedures were popular. Then scientific sanity prevailed and their treatments were ridiculed.

Attempts to defy mortality continue, which is perhaps not surprising since we live more than ever in an age which venerates youth. In her sixties the author Simone de Beauvoir realised the degradation of old age. In *The Coming of Age* she wrote, 'It is old age, rather than death, that is to be contrasted with life. Old age is life's parody, whereas death transforms life into destiny.' Old age should offer the opportunity to reflect on the lessons of a life. Unfortunately, all too often the reality of old age is a struggle between health and disease. Senile dementia strikes at one person in five over the age of 80; the incidence of cancer in humans doubles about every nine years between the ages of 45 and 80; the chances of dying of a heart attack in the US are about 200 times greater for a 50-year-old man than a teenager.

The good news is that it is becoming clear that old age does not inevitably arrive hand in hand with decline and decay. Human ageing has at last become a field for reputable scientific study, bringing together researchers from many different disciplines. The array of questions to be answered is long and hard, spanning the entire spectrum of human biology, but answers are being found which indicate that not only should it be possible to alleviate the problems that accompany old age, it should also be possible to extend our lifespan far in excess of its present limits. Control of the ageing process would allow doctors to lengthen our lives and give us the same resilience in old age that we possess in youth — as an editorial in the *Journal of the American Medical Association* put it, 'to die young late in life.' This may sound hopelessly futuristic, but our present scientific knowledge about ageing requires us to dispense with many myths, the first of which is the immutability of the ageing process itself.

Over 40 years ago Clive McCay of Cornell University found that if he drastically underfed young rats, giving them just enough food to enable them to survive, he could extend their usual lifespans by a third, and for most of this extended lifespan the rats remained healthy and active. In the early 1970s Roy Walford of the University of California achieved similar results with fish, by lowering their body temperatures. These discoveries, along with many others that this book sets out to explain, point towards the inescapable conclusion that ageing is susceptible to control in the same way as any other process taking place in our minds and bodies.

There is now an increasing optimism among scientists that just as the early twentieth century saw tremendous strides in the field of physics, the closing of this century may be marked by an unravelling of the mysteries of old age, and a total change in the nature of medicine. Behind this hope lies not the vanity of twentieth-century man, but the economic necessity of twenty-first-century man.

In the United Kingdom, the Government estimates that 75 per cent of the male children now being born will live to be 65 or older, while 85 per cent of female children will see their 65th birthdays. It is a pattern which is being repeated throughout Europe and America, and inevitably it will lead to steeply increasing numbers of old people. The ageing of the baby boom generation will exacerbate the current trend towards an older America; there are at present 26.6 million over the age of 65, representing 11 per cent of the whole population. In the half century from 1980 to 2030, the population of senior citizens is expected to rise by 120 per cent, compared with an increase of 24 per cent in the population younger than age 65. Such developments have the potential to bring with them enormous problems. Already in the UK one-third of hospital beds on any given night are occupied by patients aged over 65; in the USA the over 65s, who count for a little under one-ninth of the population, are responsible for one-third of the nation's medical bills. Unless the means can be found to allow older people to live healthier, more independent lives, vast resources will have to be channelled into supporting an ever-growing population of old people who are sick and bedridden.

The need for a solution to this problem is not confined to the small group of privileged countries that constitute the developed world. As one might expect, the number of people in the developing countries who live to see their 65th birthday is far lower than in the richer western countries, standing at just 3 per cent of the population even in the most rapidly developing countries like Brazil and India. In the tropical and sub-tropical world old people are even more of a rarity, and there are many countries in Africa, Asia and Central America where the percentage of the population who live to 65 is as low as 2 per cent. Nevertheless, slowly improving living conditions and the effects of modern medicines are starting to make themselves felt. The United Nations is predicting that by the year 2025 there will be as many people over the age of 31 as there are under that age. Even more startling is that the United Nations believes that within this period the number of people in the world aged over 60 will almost treble – from 400 million to 1.1 billion. Unless older people can be given their independence the hard-pressed Third World will soon have hundreds of millions of extra unproductive mouths to feed.

The prospect of a rapidly greying world means that governments are diverting resources into age-related research. This trend has been particularly spectacular in the USA, where over the last decade Washington has increased funding for the National Institute on Ageing from 19 million dollars a year to 140 million dollars a year. According to the Research of Ageing Act, which founded the Institute in 1976, the Congress finds and declares that:

1. the study of the ageing process, the one biological condition common to all, has not received support commensurate with its effects on the lives of every individual;

2. in addition to the physical infirmities resulting from advanced age, the economic, social and psychological factors associated with ageing operate to exclude millions of older people from the full life and the place in our society to which their years of service and experience

entitle them;

3. recent research efforts point the way toward alleviation of the problems of old age by extending the healthy middle years of life;

4. there is no American institution that has undertaken comprehensive systematic and intensive studies of the bio-medical and behavioural aspects of ageing and the related training of necessary personnel;

5. the establishment of a National Institute on Ageing within the National Institutes for Health will meet the need for such an institution.

The formation of the Institute owes much to the efforts of US Senator Alan Cranston, a former track star at Stanford University who at the age of 55 ran a 100-yard sprint in just 12.5 seconds and in 1975, when he was 60, won the 'King of Capitol Hill' bicycle race between members of Congress.

The opening of the Institute added a new urgency to age-related research and marked the coming-of-age of gerontology, the scientific study of the ageing process. While gerontology tries to understand ageing by investigating the basic science behind the way our minds and bodies change with time, geriatric medicine approaches the problem from a different angle, finding methods to cope with the breakdown of health that often comes with old age. Like gerontology, geriatric medicine is now enjoying a new importance.

In Britain the roots of geriatric medicine can be traced back to the Poor Relief Act of 1601, which was the first example of community care for old people. The Act authorised local parishes to levy a tax on property owners to pay for the care of the poor, the chronically sick and the aged. For old people, inclusion with the poor was an unfortunate step whose effects were to be felt for hundreds of years, particularly during the economic slump of the mid-nineteenth century, when the life led by working people sank to a level little better than that led by paupers in the workhouse. The politicians responded by setting up the 1832 Royal Commission on the Poor Law, which, under the chairmanship of the Bishop of London, came up with the principle of 'less eligibility'. In the words of the

Commission's Secretary Edwin Chadwick, '... every penny bestowed that tends to render the condition of the pauper more eligible than that of the independent labourer is a bounty on indolence and vice'. The resultant measures, intended to discourage the poor from seeking refuge in the workhouse, had grave implications for the old, and although it was decided that special provision should be made for 'the aged poor of good conduct', this often did not materialise. Throughout the nineteenth century, and into the early twentieth century, the workhouse remained a dreaded institution which, out of necessity, became the last refuge for many old people.

It was not until the 1930s that the pioneers of geriatric medicine began their work. They showed that if proper medical care was given to the sick and bedridden confined within the workhouse infirmaries, then some were able to leave their beds, the majority became partially independent, and some were once again able to live in the outside world. Since then geriatric medicine has evolved to provide a complex range of care for the often inter-related diseases that come with old age. Its achievements have not always received the publicity that they have deserved. We know now, for example, that some of the physical and mental problems characteristic of old age are actually diseases that can be prevented or treated. Senility is not an inevitable companion of old age, but rather the sign of a diseased brain. One-quarter of all cases of senile dementia are curable. In these cases thyroid problems or brain tumours are the cause of chronic forgetfulness and confusion. Of the cases that are not reversible, slightly more than half are caused by Alzheimer's disease, about one-fifth by strokes and the rest by a combination of these two. As we will see later, intensive research is now pointing a way towards a cure for all types of senility. Osteoporosis, the weakening of bones in old age that is a leading killer of the elderly, is thought to be preventable by a regime including more calcium in the diet, encouraging exercise, and administering hormones to women who suffer the disorder after the menopause.

Geriatric medicine and gerontology are complementary. As geriatricians increase their knowledge of the diseases which accompany old age, they inevitably discover information that helps gerontologists tackle the problem of why disease and disability are far more likely to strike at old people. Geriatric medicine can offer immediate help to millions of people, but in the end the best way to combat the problems of old age must be to gain a measure of control over the ageing process itself. This is a challenge new to medicine and to meet it we have to start by understanding why, and how, more and more people are living longer.

Contrary to popular myth, medicine can only claim a small part of the credit for raising our chances of seeing old age. In 1300 the population of England and Wales stood at about four million. Then came the Black Death of 1348 to 1350, a bubonic plague transmitted by fleas which lived on rats and people. Its effects were devastating. By 1377, the next year for which there are reliable figures, the population had almost halved, standing at a fraction over two million. Not until the middle of the sixteenth century did the population manage to regain its pre-Black Death levels, and in 1700 the population still stood at just over five million. As late as 1735, the death rate was still capable of outstripping the birth rate, causing the population to fall. Yet between 1735 and 1850 the population of England and Wales almost quadrupled, reaching 18 million, a phenomenon that was repeated throughout the whole of Europe. The eighteenth century saw no great medical advances able to explain such a large scale improvement in health. Few people were able to visit hospitals, and anyway, it is doubtful whether the hospital care of that time would have done much for anyone's hopes of survival. No diseases were eradicated and vaccination had still to be discovered. It seems that most of the credit for the population explosion should be given to the tremendous strides made by eighteenth century agriculture, in particular the growing of crops for winter feed. Until then only breeding cattle could be kept alive during the winter, the remainder having to be slaughtered and salted. Fresh meat, more vegetables and more milk in winter all helped to reduce the enormous number of deaths that took place during childhood.

There is also another, more subtle, explanation for the sudden growth in population. During the period 1500 to 1730 young people were far more likely to die than in either the preceding or succeeding years. It is possible to guess at the reasons for this check on the population. At the end of the fifteenth century, syphilis entered Europe in a form far more infectious than today's; in the sixteenth century smallpox changed its nature and became far more dangerous; and a mysterious illness known as the English Sweat (possibly a type of influenza) appeared in 1485 and continued to cause lethal epidemics. However, by the middle of the eighteenth century, these diseases, for whatever reason, were no longer the killers they once were. The disappearance of three virulent diseases combined with revolutionary advances in agriculture must have given population growth a powerful stimulus. After 1850 the population increase became ever more remarkable, with medicine and public hygiene now playing a far more important part. The population of England and Wales rose from 23 million in 1876 to 32 million in 1900. Quite simply more and more people began to survive much longer. Doctors were available to all classes of society. Hospitals successfully treated diseases rather than simply isolated them. Prevention of some diseases was possible and, above all, the cause of many had been discovered, so that, for instance, polluted water supplies no longer led to outbreaks of cholera and typhoid. Scientific medicine combined with better sanitation, clean water and cheap food to build a healthier and longer-lived society.

This trend continued into the twentieth century. At the turn of the century, a newly-born baby could expect to live to be 47; nowadays a female child would expect to live to be 77, a male child until 71; an increase in life expectancy larger than the increase which took place over the whole of the previous 2,000 years. The reason for this jump is the way that childhood diseases have been brought firmly under control, so that killers like pneumonia, diphtheria, diarrhoea and typhoid no longer make childhood fraught with danger. In 1900 the infant mortality rate in the UK was 156 deaths for every 100,000 births. By 1983 that figure stood at 10.1.

Despite such achievements, there is one area in which modern medicine has had no impact. The average life expectancies of both men and women have increased by leaps and bounds, but there has been no corresponding increase in the age reached by the *oldest* members of society. There seems to be a barrier, a 'maximum lifespan' of around 135 years, beyond which no one can pass, no matter how healthy they and the community around them may be. If this seems far-fetched consider two times and places which offer extreme contrasts of poverty and affluence, disease and good health. In the British India of the 1920s there was an appallingly high infant mortality rate, with only half the population managing to reach the age of 20. In contrast, half the population of England and Wales in the 1960s could expect to reach their 75th birthdays. Despite this enormous difference, an analysis of births and deaths reveals a startling area of similarity: in both cases the oldest people in each population reached roughly the same age – between 100 and 120 years. So although there was a huge difference in life expectancy, there was no difference in maximum lifespan. This shows that the same ageing processes are at work in all of us, and that the superior health care of England and Wales did not, and does not, allow people to live to be 150 or even 250 years old.

It is tempting to imagine that as we improve our knowledge of how to cure diseases we will be able to push back the maximum lifespan barrier. However, conventional medicine is engaged in a battle with diminishing returns. Recent medical advances such as the discovery of antibiotics, insulin, and vaccines for diseases like polio have increased our life expectancies by far less than one might expect, and it has been estimated that all the medical advances of the last 50 years have increased life expectancy by just five years. Curing one disease does not mean that another automatically leaps in to take its place. In the USA, while cardiovascular disease (the leading cause of death) has declined by 12 per cent among over-65s since 1965, deaths from cancer, the second-leading cause of death, have shown only a modest one per cent increase. This decline in cardiovascular disease has led to a slight increase in life expectancy. Even if we eliminated the top four causes of death in humans today (heart disease, cancer, and strokes together with influenza and pneumonia) life expectancy would probably only increase by 20 years. Furthermore, this additional 20 years of life would not be 20 years of good health, but 20 years of growing infirmity. The underlying process of ageing would continue, and new age-related diseases and disabilities would emerge. According to a recent report, at least 30 per cent of the deaths of people older than 85 years are not caused by disease, but by an inability to cope with infections and traumas that would be considered minor in a younger person. Curing the diseases which presently kill us is never going to allow us to live beyond 135. Only by altering the ageing process itself will we be able to break through the maximum lifespan barrier.

It is not only the human species that has a maximum lifespan. Even plants seem to have a natural limit to their lives. Bristlecone pines in California live to be around 4,900 years old; they are older than the pyramids. The Sierra Redwood lives to the ripe old age of 2,300; while the English oak manages 1,300 years. After studying circular clumps of creosote bushes, a Californian botanist discovered that one particular creosote bush began growing in the Mojave desert almost 12,000 years ago. If correct, this would make it the oldest living plant on earth and may help explain how desert vegetation regrew after the last Ice Age. When animals are allowed to live out their lifespan there also seems to be a maximum age for each species. A mayfly lives out its entire life in the space of a single day. The longest-lived house fly lives for six weeks, a shrew for 18 months and a mouse for three years. Domestic cats are generally longer lived than dogs; the oldest cat ever recorded lived to be 36 while 29 is the maximum for dogs. The oldest elephant recorded lived to the age of 69; the Galapagos tortoise can outlive us all and reach the age of 150.

Of course stories about human Methuselahs who defy science and mortality, and happily live far beyond the age of 130, continue to circulate. They are usually spread by disreputable sections of the 'Life Extension' industry who like to give the impression that Shangri-La exists in far-off lands. In the US in particular, millions of dollars are spent by millions of people on creams and potions which claim, without any scientific evidence, to postpone the onset of old age. Keeping alive the myth that some people are able to live through the maximum lifespan barrier adds credibility to this modern day alchemy. However, none of the Methuselahs stand up to examination.

Not even the tombs in Westminster Abbey can be believed. Thomas Parr's gravestone in the Abbey announces that his life spanned 'the reigns of the ten kings' between 1483 and 1635, a period of 152 years. The story of Parr's life – and death – has come down to us from the man who carried out the post-mortem on Parr: William Harvey, physician to Charles I and the discoverer of blood flow. According to Harvey, the body of Old Parr, as he was known, was in an excellent state of preservation. It was muscular and hairy, the chest broad and strong, and the brain 'very firm and hard to the touch'. According to Harvey, Old Parr lived 152 years and nine months in the parish of Salop in Shropshire where he lived on 'subrancid cheese, and milk in every form, coarse and hard bread and small drink, generally sour whey'. He even remarried in his 120th year and his wife 'did not deny that he had intercourse with her after the manner of other husbands with their wives, nor until about 12 years back had he ceased to embrace her frequently'. News of Old Parr's reputed age reached the Earl of Arundel, who had him carried to London in a special litter in order to show him off to King Charles I on his 150th birthday. The aged rustic was kindly treated by the Earl, wined and dined by the King and then, as Harvey puts it, he died of a 'surfeit'. This sudden intake of meat and other forbidden fruits after a life devoted to a meagre vegetarian diet seems to have killed him.

Parr's lifestyle and diet are still used by some to lend credence to the benefits of subrancid cheese – yet as far back as 1873, William Thoms, Deputy Librarian of the House of Lords, showed that there was no evidence to support the assertion that Old Parr lived to be 152. Thoms, who also disposed of the legends of Henry Henkins (169) and the Countess of Desmond (140) wrote rather wearily, 'let no-one who has the slightest desire to live in peace and quietness be tempted, under any circumstances, to enter upon the chivalrous task of trying to correct a popular error'. The same is just as true today.

Claims for immense longevity still spring from the natives of isolated communities like Vilacamba in Ecuador, the Hunza tribe in India, and the Caucasus Mountains in the USSR. Despite immense scientific efforts no one has been able to authenticate any of these claims.

In the early twentieth century a British doctor travelled to Hunza, a community of a few thousand people tucked away in the Himalayan foothills of northern Pakistan at an altitude of 8,000 feet. While working for the Indian Medical Service, Dr Robert McCarrison was amazed at the health and well-being of the natives, and commented on their long life. McCarrison decided that the 'unsophisticated foods of nature' the Hunzas ate were responsible for increased longevity.

More recently, a cardiologist at the University of Minnesota carried out a study on 11 centenarians among the Hunzas. He described them as small, about 5 feet 3 inches tall, weighing about 100 pounds, and eating less than 1,500 calories a day. He found few signs of obvious ageing among the elderly Hunzas, who walk daily up and down a 500-foot hill, eat very little meat but lots of apricots and chilli peppers, and drink wine and glacial water that is rich in selenium and other minerals. However, none of them had exceeded the maximum lifespan.

The Russians promoted their longevity claims by issuing a postage stamp of a resident of Georgia when he had reached the remarkable age of 148. He apparently went on to live for another 20 years. There were supposedly nearly 9,000 centenarians living in the Caucasus Mountains in Russia, 500 of whom were thought to be older than 120. However, the longevity bubble was burst when Dr Zhores Medvedev, a Russian gerontologist, uncovered the geriatric fraud and discovered that the ageing individuals were not as old as they seemed and had falsified their ages. For example, he showed that life expectancy in Georgia is no higher than anywhere else in Russia, and in recent years the number of centenarians in the area had fallen.

Presumably it is no coincidence that in such societies old age is revered, and the older you get the more incentive there is to exaggerate your age. Even without the added impetus of increased social standing old people tend to lie about their age. The most reliably pedigreed group of people in the world, the British peerage, has in 10 centuries produced only two peers who reached their hundredth birthdays – and only one of these celebrated his one hundred and first. Better record keeping is slowly leading to a decline in longevity claims. At one time the *Guinness Book of Records* listed Charlie Smith as the USA's oldest person. He supposedly celebrated his 137th birthday on 4 July 1979. Efficient record keeping led to the demise of Charlie Smith: a previously unknown marriage certificate revealed that he had exaggerated his age by at least 33 years. The latest figures suggest that he was still two months short of his hundredth birthday when he died on 7 October 1979.

The oldest person to have lived in modern times is a man, Shigechiyo Izumi, who lives on the remote Japanese island of Tokunishima. He was born in 1865 during the rule of Japan's last Shogun, and he was listed as being six years old in the census of 1871. In 1985, when he celebrated his 120th birthday, Izumi was still alert and healthy, able to recall both the events of the previous day, and the events of his childhood over a century before. He still had his eyesight although one eye had been damaged by a wood chip sixty years earlier. Since his eighties he had been without teeth or dentures. However, his electrocardiogram (ECG) was not completely normal, and his doctors believe that he may have had a heart attack when he was 114. Three years later he suffered a serious bout of pneumonia, but he recovered with the help of antibiotics. Apart from this he reached the age of 120 encountering few illnesses.

Izumi is an extreme example of how it is impossible to predict the vigour of an old person merely on the basis of their age. His impressive longevity could be due to genetics or his peculiar lifestyle; he gave up smoking when he was 116, but took up drinking at the age of 70. Like Old Parr, Izumi's diet was mainly vegetarian.

The oldest person known to have lived in Britain is Anna Williams, who on 12 July 1985 reached the age of 112 years. Although eight years younger than Izumi, at the age of 112 she was blind, and walking with the aid of a frame. In turn Mrs Williams was far more vigorous than many 80-year-olds.

This sort of extreme variability is reflected in the fact that Ronald Reagan was re-elected President of the United States at the age of 73, and that Katharine Hepburn's performance in *On Golden Pond* won her an Oscar, again at the age of 73. Chronological age is not a reliable indicator of how a person feels or how they function. Only when we know how to measure the rate of ageing in a particular individual can we see if a particular therapy is slowing the speed at which ageing takes place. To study ageing we must be able to measure it.

The straightforward approach towards monitoring how age alters the human body might appear to be to compare a group of old people with a group of young people, with a few days of physical and mental tests soon revealing the differences caused by ageing. Unfortunately, except at a superficial level, this approach does not reveal very much. Imagine that it was discovered that old people have less cholesterol in their bodies than young people. This could be the result of ageing but it could also mean that people with a lot of cholesterol in their blood never reach old age. Studies like this do not compare like with like. An 80-year-old mathematics professor may have far more mental agility than many younger people. A former athlete may still be able to hold his own against an untrained man half his age. What is needed is a 'longitudinal' study in which a series of tests are carried out on the same set of people over a long period of time.

In 1958 Dr Nathan Shock started such a study, and the Baltimore Longitudinal Study is now a textbook example of how the ravages of old age should be studied. Dr Shock recruited 660 volunteers, aged between 20 and 96, and over the following years he and his co-workers have been studying the minds and bodies of the volunteers as they alter with time. Some of the original volunteers are now dead, but fresh recruits have swelled the ranks of the study to 630 men and 150 women. Every two years each of these people undergoes three days of tests designed to discover age-related changes. The results of this study, and of many subsequent studies, have revealed the basic pattern of how we grow old, and have to some extent enabled us to disentangle the universal effects of old age from the effects of disease and illness.

The earliest signs of advancing age are those which keep the cosmetics industry in business. Our skin becomes less elastic and unable to smooth out wrinkles, and blemishes form because an ageing pigment is laid down. The small blood vessels close to the skin become more delicate, and they become increasingly likely to break and cause bruising. Both men and women begin to lose their hair, leading to partial or complete baldness. The hair that remains greys and whitens with age. All of this is familiar, but age causes a pattern of change that goes far deeper. It is a pattern that does not always fit in with our preconceived notions. The effect of age on the brain is complex. Different areas of the brain and spinal cord are affected at different rates so that, for example, pain can still be appreciated when other sensory stimuli, such as the ability to perceive extremes in temperature, are lost. Memory also declines, and reaction times get slower. The brain loses as much as three ounces in weight by the time we reach the age of 60, but learning new tasks is still possible, although the process might take a little longer. On the whole it seems you should 'use it or lose it'. As we will see later in this book, recent experiments have shown that when elderly rats are kept in a stimulating environment the brain cells in some areas respond by forging new connections. Day by day, evidence is growing that development and growth in the brain can go on well into old age, provided life is still posing some mental challenges.

The heart weakens with old age and pumps less blood, causing the circulation rate to slow. This does not mean that every old person is likely to suffer heart failure, since the heart usually remains strong enough to cope with most of the body's demands. In the West, cholesterol levels rise, leaving fatty deposits that clog up the blood vessels and contribute to the increase in blood pressure that often comes with age.

As we grow older, our bones become thinner and more brittle, so that fractures are more likely to occur. Calcium salts are often deposited in cartilages and ligaments, shrinking them and making them less elastic. This particularly affects the cartilage discs between the vertebrae of the spine, and explains why people in their seventies and eighties lose some height. The joints of older people also show changes with age, but usually this does not cause disability unless a disease like arthritis is present.

Muscle co-ordination starts to fail with age, and so an older person's movements are often slower and less accurate than when they were young. The muscles also begin to waste, and this loss of bulk explains why older people characteristically have thin limbs, and hollows in their hands. Overall, the changes wrought by age on muscles and bones contribute to the posture many older people adopt: a stooping gait, with bent arms, and the head and neck held a little in front of the body.

Just as the skin becomes less elastic, so do the lungs and ribcage. This affects the amount of air that we can breathe into our lungs, so that older people often become short of breath even when they are in perfect health. The number of microscopic sacs, known as alveoli, in each lung also decreases and the thickness of the alveoli walls increases. Since oxygen from the air passes through the walls of the alveoli into the blood stream, their increased thickness and fewer number slows the rate at which oxygen passes into the blood, contributing to a shortage of breath.

The membranes of the bowel and the muscles surrounding them atrophy in later life. This means that the normal onward movement – peristalsis – of food particles through the gut slows, but not to a sufficient extent to cause any delay in the emptying of the stomach. Older people also secrete fewer gastric juices, but this is in itself insufficient to explain the many digestive problems they suffer. Constipation, by far the most common, may well be caused by the decrease in peristalsis, coupled with a lack of fibre in the diet.

The kidneys deteriorate considerably with age, so that the filtering ability of an 89-year-old may be half that of a 20-year-old. Luckily this change rarely matters: assuming there is no disease present the kidney is still able to cope with the body's usual requirements. Incontinence is not an inevitable companion of ageing; it is the result of disease.

The reproductive organs atrophy after the menopause in women, later in men. Their procreative powers are also lost, although this happens to a lesser extent in men: many septuagenarians have been able to father children. There is also some decline in function of the endocrine glands, the ductless glands which secrete hormones directly into the bloodstream. In particular the pituitary gland and the thyroid gland are known to have a diminishing output of hormones during later years.

Old people are often long-sighted because of changes in the

lens in the eyeball. Degenerative changes also take place in the retina, the light-sensitive layer of the eyeball upon which the lens casts its image, but few people lose their sight. Cataracts are a more serious threat. Most old people also have little trouble hearing conversations at normal pitch, although they might have problems with sounds at higher frequencies. At the age of about 50 there is also a decline in the acuteness of the sense of taste, and at 60 the sense of smell starts to fail.

All of these changes contribute to the decreased resilience experienced by old people as they grow older, and the body's defences against disease also decline with age (that is why pneumonia is such a common cause of death among the elderly, but not among younger people). In fact, not only do the body's defences fail, they also begin to turn on the body itself. There is now evidence that malfunctions in the immune system are involved in major diseases of old age like cancer and heart disease. Whether the decline in the immune system is a result of ageing, or the cause of ageing, is a matter of fierce debate to which we will return later. However, what is indisputable is that studies like those in Baltimore show that the processes involved affect different organs and functions at different rates. It is not just people that age at different rates, different parts of the same person also age at different rates. A person with 'young lungs' may have an 'old heart'; an agile mind may be accompanied by an ageing body.

Gerontologists approach the problem of following the speed at which a particular function or organ ages by giving it a 'functional age'. A 45-year-old whose lungs perform as well as the average 35-year-old has lungs with a functional age of 35. The same man may have a liver with a functional age of 50. One of the simplest tests of functional age is for the skin. To see how fast it is ageing, pinch the back of your hand and see how long it takes to become smooth again. If your skin has a functional age of under 45, it will take less than two seconds. If its functional age is between 45 and 65 it will take between two and 20 seconds to return to normal whilst a time between 20 and 50 seconds indicates a functional age for your skin of between 65 and 75.

The next step in measuring how we age is to assign each

person an overall 'biological age'. This is done by taking a number of functional ages associated with a particular person, and comparing them with the statistical norm for someone of the same calendar age. A well-preserved person of calendar age 65 might find themselves with a biological age of 55. The increasing sophistication of such calculations is not a response to personal vanity. As gerontological research progresses, scientists will want to test potential anti-ageing therapies – a drug, perhaps, or a new diet, or an exercise regime. Monitoring the effect the therapy has on a person's biological age will provide the litmus test of any such therapy, and the calculations behind biological ages are becoming increasingly reliable, although questions do remain about which functional ages should be fed into the calculations, and what weight they should be given. As well as testing anti-ageing therapies, biological age can also be used to investigate how lifestyle may affect the rate of ageing. Already researchers have discovered that married men tend to have lower biological ages than single men of the same calendar age – although whether this is a comment on the benefits of marriage or the type of men women find most attractive remains open to speculation!

Measuring how we age is far easier than understanding the forces that cause us to age. The puzzle for scientists has been to explain why the lifespan of higher organisms should be limited, when there seems no reason in principle why it could not be extended, perhaps indefinitely. It is perhaps natural, therefore, to suppose that ageing serves a useful purpose and that, in some subtle way, it is an evolutionary adaptation. One suggestion is that if organisms did not age they would eventually overcrowd their environment, and resources like food would become exhausted. One drawback with this theory is that mortality in animals living wild – through accidents, infections or being eaten by predators – is usually so great that individuals rarely live long enough to show signs of old age. Ageing is not needed as a way to prevent overcrowding, because environmental mortality ensures that the population is kept in check. A second suggestion is that it is necessary for a species to have a finite lifespan because this guarantees a turnover of generations, with individuals dying and being replaced by their offspring. The rare mutations which occur among their descendants could then be acted upon by natural selection giving the opportunity for the species to adapt to any changes in its environment. The only problem is, if, as already explained, ageing is not something normally found in the wild, then clearly natural selection cannot have operated directly to bring it about. Many investigators now believe that ageing is not of benefit in itself, but arises as an accidental byproduct of some other kind of evolutionary process.

The way in which old age appears throughout the entire body has led researchers to conclude that ageing is driven by events taking place within the human cell, the basic building block of the body. In fact as far back as 80 years ago, well before the Baltimore Study, scientists were speculating that cells themselves may undergo an ageing process. But then came a major stumbling block.

Most human cells reproduce by dividing over and over again, providing fresh cells to repair damage caused by the wear and tear of daily living. In 1912 Alexis Carrel, one of the foremost biologists of his day, started to grow a culture of tissue cells taken from chicken hearts. In his laboratory in New York, he and his co-workers fed the cells with a special mixture containing extract of chicken embryo, and as expected the cells started to divide. The cells continued to divide for the next 34 years; they only stopped when, two years after Carrel's death, the culture was thrown away. By then it seemed that Carrel, who had already won a Nobel Prize for discovering how to sew blood vessels together, had established an important principle of gerontology: in an ideal environment cells are immortal. This led scientists to conclude that ageing in organisms must be due to interactions between cells, or to some central mechanism, hormonal perhaps, whose influence pervades the body. Since cells did not age, ageing could not have its roots in processes taking place inside cells.

There matters remained until 1961. In that year Leonard Hayflick and Paul Moorehead showed that human cells only have the capacity to divide about 50 times – a result in direct contradiction with Carrel's findings. Hayflick and Moorehead took pieces of lung tissue from a human embryo and used digestive enzymes to split the tissue into individual cells. The cells were washed and put into nutrient bottles at room temperature. They divided regularly, but as the fiftieth division approached the cells divided more and more slowly and changed their appearance. Finally they would not divide at all, and the cells died, having reached their 'Hayflick limit' of 50 divisions. In effect a human cell has a built-in lifespan. As the finding was repeated over and over again by many other scientists, it became clear that Alexis Carrel and his co-workers had for over 30 years inadvertently introduced fresh chicken cells into their culture when they added the nutrient extract of chicken embryo. Hayflick's discovery gave a tremendous boost to research efforts and refocused interest in the cell.

Fresh experiments have since shown that cells taken from young people are able to go through more divisions than those taken from older people. As a person grows older their cells lose the ability to divide and replace themselves, an effect which is also found in animal cells. Furthermore, cells taken from long-lived species like the Galapagos tortoise are able to divide more often than cells taken from a short-lived species like the mouse. The maximum lifespan of a species correlates with the ability of its cells to divide and replace themselves.

Ever since Leonard Hayflick's seminal experiment gerontologists have been exploring this link between ageing and cell division. Why, for example, do human tissue cells grow old and die, while cancer cells live for ever? The search for the key to immortality has moved to within the human cell.

CHAPTER TWO

Old Father Time

Progeria is a strange and devastating disease. Children who fall victim to it accelerate towards old age while their contemporaries are just reaching puberty; by some quirk of fate physical time is compressed and the ageing process goes out of control. Like the existence of the Hayflick limit, discussed in Chapter One, this disease underlines the importance of the human cell in ageing.

In some cases the disease, which occurs once in every eight million births, is so severe that victims appear to age by five years every six months. It is a progressive decline which in many ways mirrors the ageing process, internally as well as externally. At birth children with progeria appear normal, but at about six months to one year of age they begin to lose their hair and fatty tissue. With time they become totally bald, losing their eyebrows and often their eyelashes. Hearing and eyesight fail, and they start to develop diseases associated with old age like arthritis, cataracts and high blood pressure. By the time they have reached the height of an average five-year-old and the weight of an average three-year-old they have stopped growing. As with many elderly patients, the cause of death is usually heart failure or overwhelming infection. So far, no one with progeria has survived beyond their early thirties. It is a disease that is not defined by race or sex but is thought to stem from a genetic defect.

Doctors have always hoped that studying progeria might reveal some of the secrets of the ageing process. They have had no such good fortune: attempts to find the molecular basis for the rapid ageing of these children have been largely unsuccessful. Most of the chemical products found in the blood or urine of ageing individuals are present in normal quantities in patients with progeria.

However, there has been one major, tantalising discovery. Skin cells taken from progeria victims have much shorter lifespans than cells taken from normal children. Also, the number of divisions they go through before dying is similar to those for cells taken from old people. This is an important finding because, along with a great deal of other evidence, it shows that progeria and the associated ageing process are linked to the progress of individual cells towards their Hayflick limits.

It is now accepted as a general rule that skin cells from a young person will undergo more divisions before they die than cells taken from an older person. These laboratory experiments suggest that the older we get, the closer our cells move towards their Hayflick limit. When these experiments were first carried out critics argued that the cells stopped dividing not because of any in-built ageing limit, but because of some experimental error. An elegant experiment carried out by Leonard Hayflick disproved this.

Taking advantage of the fact that normal skin cells from male and female embryos can be distinguished by comparing their sex chromosomes, he mixed female cells that were only 10 divisions old with male cells that had already divided 40 times. After 20 population doublings the cultures were examined. Only female cells were still dividing; the male cells had run out of time when they reached their Hayflick limit. Ageing had led to its inevitable conclusion.

The limited lifespan of human cells has now been measured in cells taken from a number of tissues including brain, liver, muscle, and of course, skin. No exception has yet been found to the general rule that normal cells possess a limited ability to divide, and that limit seems to be 50.

Leonard Hayflick also discovered that this limit is deeply ingrained in the memory of the cell. If skin cells taken from human embryos are frozen in liquid nitrogen at the tenth doubling and later thawed, they will undergo 40 more doublings and then stop. If they are frozen at the twentieth doubling then they will go through another 30 divisions before they die. When the doublings before and after freezing are added up, the total is always the magic figure of 50. This memory is remarkably good; one of Hayflick's human cell strains remembered this after more than 20 years in liquid nitrogen.

The scientists running the Baltimore longitudinal study (see Chapter One) are now freezing cells so that they can compare cells taken from young subjects with cells taken from the same person years later. It is like being reminded of one's youth while in middle age, and may give new insights into the nature of ageing.

Most scientists now agree that changes in the cells of our body lie at the root of the ageing process. We do not live longer than other animals because we have larger bodies, or because we are constructed differently. Although lifespan does have links with other factors like body size and metabolic rate, it is the cell that has become the focus of the search for the cause of ageing.

Of course this doesn't mean to say that what goes on in a test tube accurately reflects the changes happening inside the body as we get older. To see if the Hayflick limit operates inside, as well as outside the body, cells have been transplanted between young and old animals. Inbred strains of rats are rather like identical twins in that one animal will not reject a graft from another. When young cells were transplanted into young, inbred rats they carried on dividing and even outlived their original donor. Only after being successfully transplanted into seven different rats did the cells begin to slow down as they started to age. Eventually they stopped growing altogether. This shows that even in a 'young' body, cells will age and die.

While these animal experiments proved that cells are not immortal, they also demonstrated that even with a Hayflick limit cells are capable of outliving an animal's normal lifespan. So, a direct equation between ageing and the Hayflick limit does not make sense. Fifty population doublings will generate far more cells than could possibly be required in an individual's lifetime. The cells from even the oldest human beings can still undergo at least 20 more population doublings. Nothing is easy in the field of ageing: the limited lifespan of the cells does not define the lifespan of the organism.

If skin cells from embryos get through 50 population doublings in the laboratory, and die out in a matter of months, it is only because the laboratory acts like a hot house forcing the pace of growth. In the body the cells divide at a much slower rate.

If the Hayflick limit is not the *cause* of ageing then it may be a symptom of other ageing processes that occur in the cell. This idea was reinforced when it was realised that skin cells grown in test tubes start to slow down and age well before they stop dividing. These ageing changes include the way the cell breaks down food, repairs damage, and produces and uses energy. It is probable that it is these sorts of changes that lie at the root of ageing and eventual death.

The body is made up of several hundred million cells. Each one is a self-contained unit, taking in food and converting it into energy and waste products. To function efficiently, these processes are carried out by a number of complex structures each with its own role to play. The largest and most obvious is the cell's control centre, the nucleus, which sits in the middle of the cell surrounded by a watery fluid called cytoplasm. Inside the nucleus are a number of spiral protein filaments which during the process of cell division form threads called chromosomes. Each human cell contains 23 pairs of chromosomes. These are of great importance to the cell and the organism because they contain our genetic inheritance in the form of elements called genes. Genes are made of a chemical called deoxyribonucleic acid or DNA. Each strand of DNA contains a coded message. DNA not only controls the way life begins when the genetic message is passed on at fertilisation, but also controls the day-to-day functioning of the body after birth, instructing different parts of the cell machinery to make protein products like hormones or enzymes needed for the everyday working of the cell.

There is a series of complicated steps between the initial deciphering of the coded message and the end product coming off the production line. Accuracy is important. If the instructions contained in the DNA are misread, an incorrect product will be synthesized, and so the process is supervised by a series of enzymes which 'proof read' the assembly line at each stage. These enzymes are of course themselves made from instructions coded within the DNA.

Outside the nucleus, the surrounding fluid, the cytoplasm, contains a number of structures which manufacture the various proteins as dictated by the DNA and arrange for waste disposal. The entire cell is surrounded by a fatty outer sheath called a membrane which allows raw materials in and finished proteins out when needed. Whatever the process that limits the ability of the cell to divide more than 50 times, it must be controlled either from within the nucleus or from within the surrounding cytoplasm.

Hayflick decided to find out where in the cell that control lay. Skin cells were grown as usual in the laboratory but this time a particular chemical was added which forces the nucleus out of the cell. This was a very neat way of producing millions of cells that contained only cytoplasm. These cells are called cytoplasts and can live quite happily for days without their nucleus.

Cytoplasts from young cells were joined to old cells still with their nucleus intact and vice versa. The results were striking. Without its nucleus young cytoplasm was not able to rejuvenate old cells. Similarly old cells without a nucleus could not age young cells. The cytoplasm seemed to have no effect on a cell's rate of ageing and it was reasonable to conclude that the nucleus controls the rate at which cells divide, and so their rate of ageing.

Since these experiments were carried out techniques have been developed for transplanting nuclei into cytoplasts. In these experiments young nuclei were added to old cytoplasts and old nuclei to young cytoplasts. The *young* nuclei rejuvenated the *old* cytoplasts while the *old* nuclei aged the *young* cytoplasts, reinforcing the idea that the secret of the Hayflick limit lies within the nucleus.

Scientists have now put forward a number of theories to suggest how the nucleus could control cell ageing. Most of them believe that the answer must lie at the critical nerve centre of the nucleus in the genetic information encoded in the DNA. The precise way in which this is achieved is still a matter of some debate.

Roughly speaking, there are two different theories to explain why cells age and die: the first is that the cells are actually *programmed* to age by specific ageing genes which act like an internal clock; the other theory argues that nature has created ageing more by mistake than by design – the *unprogrammed* theory of ageing. No one can yet be sure which theory is correct – in the field of ageing research it pays to keep an open mind – although, as we will see, the unprogrammed theory probably has the upper hand at the moment.

Proponents of the unprogrammed theory of ageing suggest that ageing happens because random damage accumulates as cells continually divide. In particular the cells' DNA and proteins gradually build up errors. In the programmed theory, ageing is seen as a part of normal development governed by the genes. Every adult cell contains about 50,000 genes. In a normal cell only a very few of those genes will be called into action. This only happens as and when the cell needs the particular protein that the gene carries the recipe for. The genes that are not needed for the efficient running of the cell do nothing.

If the whole pattern of human growth and development from conception to old age, in sickness and in health, can be thought of as an orchestration of the timing in which the genes are activated to do the body's work, then according to Leonard Hayflick and other supporters of the programme theory, age changes are more than likely controlled by the genes as well.

So ageing is thought of as a continuation of the normal process that regulates the development of the animal from the moment of its conception until its sexual development. If 'ageing genes' do exist they could act by slowing or shutting down the everyday manufacturing processes in the cell to produce the pattern of change that we call ageing, such as greying of the hair, menopause and wrinkles. If ageing genes do exist they should also be susceptible to mutation.

We do not see genetic mutations in humans which lead to a longer lifespan (even though we see plenty which lead to a shorter life through diseases like multiple sclerosis, progeria and cystic fibrosis). However, work done in the USA suggests that in the next life it might be wiser to come back as a fly – particularly a fruit fly. Scientists in Detroit have doubled the lives of fruit flies, by selectively mating long-lived flies, from 70 days to 120 days, a figure that would put a fruit fly in the *Guinness Book of Records*. Since all animals inherit the genes of their parents this experiment suggests that there is a gene or genes responsible for the fly's lifespan. Even if at first sight there appear to be few similarities between the average human being and the fruit fly, (although horror movie addicts might argue differently) recent research has shown that as far as our genetic material is concerned we have more in common than ever suspected. Indeed some genetic material seems to be identical.

Some gerontologists have suggested that if an ageing gene does exist, if might exert its effects to produce the sort of decline and death of cells that takes place during the development of an embryo. This sort of programmed cell death happens while the foetus is developing in the womb; perfectly normal cells have to die in order to give an organ its final shape. For example, when the fingers and toes are developing, a paddle-shaped structure is the first thing to form. Later the cells forming the areas that would become the webs between fingers and toes die off.

It is likely that cells which die off during the development of the embryo have a 'death clock' within themselves. In the 1960s an American embryologist found that a small patch of cells always dies off during the growth of the wing in a chick embryo. He transplanted these cells to different areas of the embryo to see if their original position was directly related to their programming for death. The results showed that position had no effect on cell death: the cells died on schedule regardless of where they were. He concluded that their death must be controlled by a clock inside each cell that ticks away and defines the moment of death.

The major changes which occur inside these cells have their greatest effect on the nucleus. The cytoplasm contracts and death enzymes are activated which cut the cells' DNA into fragments so that they can no longer replicate. How these enzymes are activated is not known.

It is conceivable that similar processes could occur throughout our lives, operating at different rates in different tissues and ultimately leading to the normal age changes that increase susceptibility to disease.

If a gene or group of genes does prove to be responsible for ageing in humans, our maximum lifespan could be altered by genetic engineering: the ageing gene could be manipulated to give us longer and healthier lives. It is an idea which has some terrifying implications but it has to be faced up to: a team of American scientists have already developed techniques to change the genes inside an embryo. Their experiments really are concerned with 'mice and men' because they have produced a breed of extra-large super-mice by inserting a gene for human growth hormone into a mouse embryo.

The scientists transplanted the human gene when the mouse embryo was still in the form of a fertilised egg. Under a microscope the scientists pierced the egg with a hollow tube much thinner than a human hair and squirted in a number of copies of the modified human gene. The egg cell was them implanted back into the mother, where it divided to produce an embryo, with each new cell containing an exact copy of the altered genes in the original cell. Twenty days later the mouse was born, normally, with all of its cells containing copies of the human gene.

At the moment, the experimenters have no control over where in the animal's genetic apparatus the foreign gene becomes integrated. Sometimes it will lodge in one chromosome, sometimes in another. In early experiments there was little success in getting the foreign genes to produce a larger than normal mouse. Now the scientists feel more confident about their abilities, and are producing a greater crop of 'super-mice'.

As techniques like this become more sophisticated they will allow us to genetically alter human embryos to prevent children being born with crippling degenerative diseases. Genetic engineering of human embryos will revolutionise medicine. It is also going to raise profound ethical problems, because genetic engineering could create Aldous Huxley's chilling Brave New World, where human beings are engineered to meet pre-ordained requirements.

For the moment genetic engineering cannot be used to combat ageing because no one has yet pinpointed an ageing gene and in fact, many theoretical scientists believe that such a search will always end in failure. They argue that if indeed we have evolved a set of genes which specifically cause ageing and death, then Darwin's theory of evolution dictates that they must have some purpose. So far, no one has been able to offer a wholly convincing explanation of the purpose of ageing and death. The theoreticians argue that the first step in unravelling the cypher of age must be to establish whether ageing offers us any real advantage.

Supporters of the programme theory of ageing have traditionally offered two explanations as to why programmed ageing serves a useful evolutionary purpose. The first argument is that the organism has evolved an ageing process because in some way this is beneficial for the survival of the species. So, for example, if humans did not age, they would soon run out of space and food. Although there can be no argument that ageing prevents this from happening, it is extremely unlikely that this is the purpose of the process. That is because until recently – at least as far as evolution is concerned – we lived in the real jungle as opposed to the urban jungle, where life was tough and men were men. Disease, famine and predators posed such a threat that few people ever lived to see old age. Life, as philosopher Thomas Hobbes put it, was 'nasty, brutish and short'. All this means that there has never been any need for a mechanism to control the length of time that we spend alive. Ageing and death cannot have evolved as the answer to a problem which has never existed. Evolution comes about through real advantage, not hypothetical advantage; the 'survival of the fittest', not the theoretically fittest. The 'living space' argument does not hold up.

The second suggestion is that a limited lifespan is needed to remove 'dead wood' so that individuals will die and be replaced by their offspring. The new mutations which occur spontaneously can then be acted upon by natural selection, giving the species a chance to adapt to any changes in its environment. The drawback with this as a theory of ageing is again that populations of organisms in their wild environment do not get the chance to enjoy the luxury of ageing. What usually happens is that they get eaten by predators or killed off by disease. This leads to the same problem as before; ageing cannot have an evolutionary purpose if it is rarely seen in the wild.

Most evolutionary changes work to encourage 'survival of

the fittest', but it is difficult to see how individuals who age can survive, reproduce, and protect their young better than those who live forever. Until someone can come up with a real reason to explain why we age, many scientists will continue to believe that ageing is not a direct result of evolution. Instead it must be a byproduct of other evolutionary changes, or an accident that evolution has found no reason to remove because life in the wild has made an early death almost inevitable.

One way this may happen is through the action of genes which start off being useful early in life, but later produce harmful effects. Imagine, for example, a hypothetical gene which causes calcium to be laid down in the bones when the animal is young, but later on leads to calcium being deposited in the arteries. Back in the jungle humans possessing this gene would find it useful in the early years of life to have strong bones but would not really be troubled by hardening arteries because by that time they would almost certainly have been picked off by disease or peckish predators.

Evolution, according to this theory, behaves rather like the racing car team which adds an ingredient to the fuel which will give extra speed for 100 laps, but will then destroy the engine. As long as their races are under 100 laps in duration, the team can use the ingredient, and prosper as a result. The harmful effects to the engine are never given the opportunity to show themselves. However if the number of laps were suddenly increased to 150 it would be a different story. Some scientists believe that this is what happens during ageing. Evolution has designed us for life in the jungle, assuming that we would only manage to survive until the ripe old age of about 30. Live any longer, and the problems start coming.

This is an attractively simple idea, but so far no one has been able to find any genes which are useful early in life, but harmful later – which of course is not to say that they never will. However, most researchers are following an alternative, rather more complicated route. They are concentrating on the way an animal manages its resources, particularly the way it uses the energy produced from food. This energy has to run a number of important processes.

First of all the animal has to grow and mature to adulthood; then it has to use energy to find a mate and protect its offspring.

It must also invest a certain amount of energy in repairing and maintaining its own body. According to Tom Kirkwood at London's National Institute for Medical Research, the trade off that is particularly significant for ageing is how much energy the animal should invest in repairing damage to itself as against the amount it should invest in reproduction.

Given the risky nature of jungle life, each organism can only have a limited expectation of life. When the individual dies the resources that have been invested in repair are lost. The horns of the dilemma are that too little attention to maintenance is dangerous because the organism may run down before it has a chance to reproduce, but too high an investment of energy to prevent damage is wasteful, because there is no point in dying young in perfect health. Is it better to channel extra energy into faster growth or greater reproductive ability? Evolution sets the energy thermostat at a level of repair which is not enough to ensure indefinite survival – immortality. The trick is not to repair all the damage which arises in the body, but to ensure that the rate of accumulation of damage is slow enough never to threaten life. How high or low the thermostat is set depends upon the species. One which is top of the jungle menu would do better to funnel energy into rapid and prolific reproduction. A species which is not so tasty may profit by putting the body in for a regular service.

This theory makes a number of predictions about the nature of ageing. First, it predicts that ageing results from the accumulation of damage to the organism. Second, that species with different longevities should have corresponding differences in their levels of maintenance and repair. Thirdly it predicts that it is likely that egg and sperm cells might have special maintenance processes to protect them from this damage so that the species can continue. What is also true is that this theory, called the 'disposable soma theory', (soma is a term used to refer to the body) can take into account the idea that there are genes which can have bad effects late in life, if these genes are thought of as the ones which control the level of repair.

The essential point is that although ageing itself is clearly disadvantageous, it is balanced against the advantage of increasing the number of offspring. This argument takes us to

the point where the question is not *whether* ageing is genetically controlled but, rather, *how* this is arranged.

To try to find out more about the possible mechanisms of
genetic control, the proponents of *unprogrammed* ageing are
trying to establish whether the DNA in our cells becomes
damaged with age. Since DNA is vital not only for cell
division, but for the synthesis of all the proteins that are needed
for the cell to carry out its tasks, changes to the DNA could
lead to the sort of generalised breakdown that characterises
ageing.

At one time it was thought that DNA was very stable, and
remained unchanged throughout the life of a cell. What has
now become clear is that the DNA in every cell in our bodies is
constantly being damaged; this damage occurs naturally as the
DNA carries out its work and also because of general wear and
tear brought on by everyday life. Nature has developed special
enzymes to repair this damage. In young healthy cells DNA is
constantly reconstructed by these enzymes which cut out
incorrect or faulty sections and replace them with new ones.
During a human lifetime of 70 years, a cell's repair enzymes
may perform over a hundred billion tasks.

Even though an army of these enzymes exists solely to repair
damage to the DNA, it is thought that as we get older their
ability to detect and replace faulty sections of DNA fails. Of
course what this leaves unanswered is the exact cause of
damage to the repair enzymes themselves, and at what stage
this accumulated damage becomes critical.

Although the experimental waters are still rather muddy, it
seems that damage to DNA builds up steadily throughout life,
rather than coming in a rush later on. The only tissue which
does show an age-related increase in damage is liver tissue, and
here, paradoxically, the rush of damage occurs early in life! If,
then, the amount of damage accumulated by our DNA
depends on our DNA repair rate, long-lived species ought to
be better at repairing DNA.

In what has since become a classic experiment, Professors
Ron Hart and Richard Setlow measured the DNA repair rates
in skin cells from a variety of animals including the mouse,
human, the elephant and the hamster. They first exposed the

cells to ultraviolet light to damage segments of their DNA. The cells' DNA repair enzymes then went into action, removing the damaged segments and replacing them with new material. Hart and Setlow had previously tagged this new material with a radioactive marker, and so were able to measure the efficiency of the repair enzymes. The results showed that the DNA repair rate was much greater in long-lived humans than in short-lived mice. Longevity was therefore linked to the ability of a species to repair its DNA.

Obviously these repair mechanisms cannot be 100 per cent perfect otherwise changes in the DNA would never take place. This would mean that offspring always had exactly the same genes as their parents, and there could be no evolution. In reality evolution has opted for a compromise; enough error to permit beneficial, evolutionary change; enough repair to ensure the survival of the species. Of course if it were possible to interfere with this balance and push it more towards the rate of repair, ageing might be retarded.

This is perhaps not as far-fetched as it sounds, since scientists in Wyoming have already accomplished this – at least for a simple one-celled organism called paramecium. The organisms were first exposed to ordinary ultraviolet light to damage their DNA, and then to 'black' light, which stimulates a so-called 'photoreactivation' process which repairs the damage. What was extraordinary was that the photoreactivation process somehow increased the rate of repair so that the repair enzymes went to work not only on the original damage caused by ultraviolet light, but also repaired normal damage caused by everyday wear and tear. The end result was that the paramecium lived much longer.

Unfortunately we are not yet in a position to be able to stimulate the repair systems in human beings. What is known is that most human diseases which are genetic and have some features of accelerated ageing also involve faulty DNA repair rates. For example, people with Down's Syndrome rarely live to be older than 50. They undergo changes which we associate with ageing in areas of the body like the brain and the immune system. In the laboratory their cells only go through a small number of doublings and never reach the normal Hayflick limit. Scientists in California have now discovered that in the laboratory the cells' ability to repair damage to the DNA caused by ultraviolet light or X-rays is defective. Although it seems likely that damage to our DNA is linked to the ageing process, no one can yet explain with certainty how this link might operate. However, one of the most controversial theories is called the 'Error Theory' and was first put forward by Leslie Orgel in 1963.

This theory of ageing aims to encompass all the different types of damage that occur in different parts of the cell. It argues that when the genetic instructions contained in the DNA are translated, occasionally a mistake is made, the end result of which is the production of a faulty chemical. DNA damaged by wear and tear will ultimately lead to the same end result. As long as there are not too many faulty chemicals made, the cell can carry on as usual.

Within the same animal this process of error accumulation could vary from cell to cell. Partly this variation would reflect random factors – individual cells (like people) vary in longevity. Partly it would reflect differences in the behaviour of distinct cell types. Some highly specialised cells in the body (for example, nerves) do not divide and multiply; such cells might use only a small proportion of the DNA recipe book in their entire lives. Others, like dividing cells, would need to copy the whole of their DNA when replicating. Even so, all body cells use part or all of their DNA repeatedly, so there is plenty of opportunity for error.

According to this theory, at first most of the errors would be relatively minor – like mistakes in the production of proteins. Gradually these errors would build up and feed back into the genetic code itself, seriously damaging the DNA. The enzymes that repair damage to the DNA are themselves made from proteins, so that the damage would escalate as the repair systems themselves incorporated errors and were unable to repair the errors in the DNA. This means that faulty proteins and enzymes would build up gradually until an 'error catastrophe' resulted and the cell died.

There is a close analogy involving a photocopier. If a document is copied, and then a copy made of the copy, and then a copy made of that copy, there is a loss of information on each pass. After 20 generations, the copy is losing its clarity.

After 50 generations the copy may be almost unrecognizable. Similarly a cell has to take its copy of the DNA information, and then this information has to be copied on through many generations. Eventually, as errors accumulate, it is conceivable the cell will break down and no longer be able to process the genetic information.

Supporters of the Error Theory believe that the only place this does not happen is in the production of egg and sperm cells. Here accuracy is vital and the body deploys extra repair and proof-reading mechanisms. If egg and sperm cells started to degenerate the whole survival of the species would be put at risk.

What makes the Error Theory particularly attractive is that it also incorporates the idea that faulty proteins will be produced if DNA is damaged by outside agents. The theory can then link these agents to the ageing process. In particular the theory can explain why highly reactive molecules called free radicals often seem to be involved in the ageing process.

At first sight Professor Robin Willson and his colleagues at Brunel University in London seem to be able to perform miracles. The Professor does a passable imitation of turning water into wine; after taking a deep breath, he blows into a flat medicine bottle half-full of a colourless liquid. Nothing appears to happen. He then screws the top back on, shakes the mixture and success, the colourless liquid turns a deep port colour. When pressed, though, the Professor does admit that this is not a demonstration of divine intervention but more a clever way to interest visiting scientists – or even journalists – in the power of free radicals.

Free radicals are produced when a chemical bond in a molecule is broken. A chemical bond is made up from two electrons, and when broken in this way, each fragment holds on to one of the two electrons. Since electrons are more stable when they exist in pairs, these free radical fragments are highly reactive. In particular they have a habit of stealing an electron from other molecules to regain their missing electron. These molecules in turn are left with a single electron so they themselves become free radicals, and chain reactions can develop where a whole series of free radicals pull off electrons from passing molecules. As can be imagined, these reactions are capable of causing massive damage to human cells and tissues.

As far as the pure chemists are concerned, free radicals are old sparring partners which have long been associated with combustion and radiation, but for many years free radicals were almost completely excluded from the repertoire of the biologist or clinician. The magic bottle experiment shows how wrong this approach was. The bottle contains a complex mixture of iron salts and amino acids which is colourless. However, when someone breathes into it, the oxygen free radicals in the breath produce a rapid free radical reaction which produces a red compound changing 'water' into 'wine'.

These free radicals are found throughout the body as a byproduct of the way that we use oxygen. When we use oxygen to provide energy by breaking down food we inevitably produce some free radicals. It is a dilemma faced by all organisms that breathe oxygen; on the one hand oxygen is reactive and an ideal agent to use to burn up our food; on the other hand it produces dangerous byproducts. As long ago as 1775 Joseph Priestley, the Yorkshireman who discovered oxygen, recognised that organisms that depend on oxygen for survival walk a narrow tightrope between successful metabolism and poisoning their cells.

Work with premature babies shows clearly that too much oxygen can be toxic. Attempts 30 years ago to treat premature babies with oxygen ended when it was discovered that they developed a form of blindness; it is now thought that the blindness was caused by the production of oxygen free radicals. Today premature babies wear an oxygen electrode that automatically reads the level of oxygen in the child's blood and as soon as the extra oxygen is reduced oxygen levels rise.

It also seems that free radicals are involved with rheumatoid arthritis which affects around half a million people in the UK, and some three million people in the USA. In a healthy body, white blood cells are designed to attack foreign organisms like bacteria. As part of this attack they spray the intruder with oxygen free radicals. Rheumatoid arthritis is now thought to be caused by white cells which move into the joint and release oxygen free radicals. These attack the membrane of the joint which swells and becomes inflamed. In the end the free radicals destroy the cartilage which lies between the bone and eventually the bone itself. This can be extremely painful and eventually disabling.

To try to control the adverse effects of oxygen free radicals on the body nature has had to devise ways of protecting itself. From bacteria to human beings, each organism contains certain enzymes whose sole job is to neutralise the free radicals. The first of these protective enzymes to be discovered was called superoxide dismutase or SOD for short. This was no ordinary enzyme catalysing a reaction between molecules, but one which speeded up the mutual annihilation of two superoxide free radicals.

Two other enzymes that help defend the body against free radicals have now been discovered: catalase and glutathione peroxidase. These enzymes don't themselves react with free radicals directly, but destroy hydrogen peroxide which might otherwise react with traces of iron or copper and in so doing form free radicals. If any free radicals escape this line of defence, they will be picked up by the second line of defence which includes superoxide dismutase and the anti-oxidants, vitamins E, C and beta carotene.

Theoretically, these defence mechanisms should be enough to protect our cells from free radical damage generated inside the body, but the number and source of free radicals in our external environment is on the increase. These include radiation of all sorts and chemicals like nitrogen dioxide, solvents and pesticides.

According to scientists who believe free radicals accelerate ageing, as we get older either more free radicals are produced internally and externally, or our lines of defence weaken and fail. The net result is that damage accumulates in the cell to produce the changes we describe as ageing.

Although that damage can be caused to DNA itself, free radicals will also damage the cell membrane because it is partly made from fats. This type of oxidation reaction has long been the bane of the food industry. Even under the most sterile conditions milk or butter will go off due to attack by free radicals in the atmosphere. Beer and crisps are also susceptible.

Since light can speed up the production of free radicals, beer bottles tend to be brown and crisps are kept in the dark as long as possible to prevent free radicals turning them soggy.

In the same way, free radicals produced in the body can oxidise the fats that make up the cell membrane, changing the membrane's structure and permeability and leading to catastrophic damage. The food industry incorporates its own anti-oxidants into fat-containing products to prevent the effects of free radicals and stop the food going off. The body's own anti-oxidants are thought to perform the same function, although scientifically this is very difficult to prove.

One of the reasons for this is that free radicals have such a short life that their presence in the body is difficult to study. Without that formal scientific proof, established medicine is reluctant to acknowledge that free radicals have a role in the ageing process.

At Brunel University Professor Willson has one of the few linear accelerators in the world currently being used to study free radical reactions in biochemical systems. He creates free radicals by beaming radiation in pulses of one-fifth of a millionth of a second into a solution of chemicals. Most radicals are highly coloured, so by capturing the intensity and decay of the colour with an apparatus called a spectrophotometer, he can actually track any free radicals produced and measure the reactions in which they are involved.

Using this equipment, his research team have been able to show that vitamin E and vitamin C work together to complement each other as biological anti-oxidants. Vitamin E neutralises a free radical by donating one of its electrons which is then replaced by vitamin C.

In this way the cell uses vitamin C to regenerate vitamin E. It is possible to reinforce these findings with simple laboratory experiments using radiation or chemicals to produce free radicals. For example, when a chemical such as ferrous sulphate is added to a biological tissue such as minced liver, free radicals are released which will oxidise the fatty cell membranes in the liver. Because the free radicals produced by the reaction are coloured they are easy to see. If the test is repeated but first vitamin C or vitamin E is added then a colour change does not take place, showing that free radicals are not produced when these vitamins are present.

There is one important weakness with these laboratory experiments. They demonstrate that free radicals can be damaging and vitamins can prevent that damage – but only in the test tube. It takes a quantum leap of imagination to state that this is what is happening inside the body, which is why scientists are becoming more and more intrigued by reports of the beneficial effects of vitamins on diseases thought to be due to the effects of free radicals.

So far these reports have been concerned with vitamin E. One of the earliest showed that vitamin E could prevent the blindness that, as mentioned earlier, was found in some premature infants receiving oxygen. If the babies received vitamin E from the day of birth, the severity of the disease was lessened. It is reasonable to assume that the beneficial effects of vitamin E were due to its ability to neutralise the free radicals before they damaged the babies' eyesight.

One of the most important side effects of free radical attack on cell membranes is that chemicals are formed which are able to join the cells' protein molecules in a process known as cross linking. Ultimately the protein molecules become locked into a much larger structure and they are no longer able to perform their assigned tasks. Furthermore, these cross-linked proteins cannot be broken down by the cell and they cause even more damage by clogging up and finally choking the waste disposal system of the cell, the lysosome.

The lysosome is one of the least glamorous but most important components of the cell, because the cell is continually renewing itself. Lysosomes are able to perform the breakdown part of this sequence because they contain powerful enzymes which digest a wide range of substances. These digestive enzymes break down the materials into their basic components which can then be used to make new parts of the cell. Older cells may be less efficient at breaking down old cell material and it is not difficult to see how a drop in the activity of the lysosome could lead to an accumulation of partially degraded cell parts and a lack of sufficient material to be reused for the synthesis of new material.

Cross-linked proteins caused by free radical attack may

contribute to the general accumulation of undigested material in the lysosome. Long-lived cells in the brain, heart and liver contain undigested waste that is referred to as lipofuscin – although it is also called age pigment. This is because the amount of lipofuscin in the brain, heart and liver corresponds extremely well with your age.

Some researchers believe that as we get older more and more lipofuscin accumulates until the lysosomes burst, releasing their enzymes into the cell. This rupture would be made easier if, like the cell membrane, the fatty covering of the lysosome has been damaged by free radical attack. The enzymes from the lysosome cause havoc once they are released into the cell because they are specifically designed to break down cellular material. In particular they will cause damage to the DNA, making it hard for the cell to function. The enzymes from the ruptured lysosome also attack other lysosomes, producing a cascade of lethal enzymes. The cell will deteriorate and eventually die. It is this sort of cell death which could lead to the changes that we describe as 'ageing'. However, 'could' remains the operative word, because at the moment the experimental evidence for the role of lysosomes remains weak.

We already know that ageing is not inevitable, because some living things have the capacity to be immortal. This means that any theory that sets out to explain cellular ageing in normal cells must also have the ability to explain how this mechanism can be altered so that some cells become immortal.

Every time an amoeba – a microscopic single-celled animal – divides, one of the two cells it forms is potentially immortal, while the other has a limited lifespan. If cells from mice are grown in culture for many generations they often become immortal like the amoeba; they will go on dividing and growing for ever.

One of life's little ironies is that the only human cells to achieve true immortality are cancer cells. A tumour is descended from a single 'founder' cell, which once was perfectly normal. Somehow it undergoes a fundamental change, which allows it to escape the restrictions of the Hayflick limit so that it begins to divide and proliferate in response to some imperative of its own. Eventually it spawns billions of similarly altered cells that make up a tumour.

A good example of the ability of cancer cells to keep on dividing comes from the HE-LA strain that is used in laboratories throughout the world. It is named after its donor Henrietta Lacks, who died of cancer in 1951, and left some of her cells for posterity and cancer research. Henrietta Lacks has now achieved a curious form of immortality and notoriety since her cancer cells have been responsible for contaminating normal cultures and ruining experiments across the world. Her cells are so aggressive that for years cell cultures transferred from one laboratory to another have become accidentally contaminated by stray HE-LA cells, turning cultures that are supposed to be bone cells, kidney cells, stomach cells into HE-LA cancer cells. Henrietta's cells take over the culture and refuse to die.

The switch from normality to immortality is easily explained by the programme theories of ageing. All that needs to happen is for there to be some mutation or genetic damage which interrupts the usual genetic ageing programme. In the case of the unprogrammed damage theories the explanation hinges on the selective amounts of energy used to spare the sperm and egg cells from damage at the expense of the body. It is argued that selective repair mechanisms would protect these cells and keep them immortal while other repair systems would be switched off in the body cells to save energy, although they could feasibly be switched on again to cope with heavy-duty genetic damage or mutation. This might explain why some malignant cells resemble embryonic cells.

The second route to unprogrammed immortality is through a small change in the rate of cell division which would make the crucial difference between accumulation or repair of damage. Since the limited ability of normal cells to divide seems to be closely linked to ageing, if we could unravel the mechanism that leads to cell immortality we might be better placed to understand ageing.

It is clear that there is still a long way to go before gerontologists agree on what constitutes the fundamental driving force behind ageing. There is still no general agreement as to how ageing is best reconciled with evolutionary theory (although an increasing number of scientists are turning towards the idea of 'the disposable soma'). Research into the mechanism of cell ageing is fragmented to a bewildering degree, although it does seem clear that a variety of processes could be combining to produce the overall effect of ageing. The study of how all these interact and lead to ageing in the whole organism is still in its very early stages. However some scientists now feel confident enough to embark on the search for the Elixir of Youth.

CHAPTER THREE

Elixirs of Youth

The path to immortality is littered with the broken reputations of misguided scientists and the claims of fraudulent quacks. To prolong life is one of mankind's oldest and most compelling dreams, but the search for an elixir of youth has attracted an unlikely collection of seekers.

In the early twentieth century, the search for the biological equivalent of the Holy Grail was dominated by the 'Gland Grafters', and like any new club, its membership was limited and exclusive. It was founded in 1889 on the extravagant claims of Professor Brown-Séquard who, like many researchers after him, tested out his experimental technique on himself. As mentioned in Chapter One, although Brown-Séquard, or even Brown-Séquard's wife, might have been very impressed with the results of his rejuvenation, the scientific community, not known for its charity or sense of humour, remained unmoved. The Professor died a few years later, his academic reputation forever clouded.

After Brown-Séquard's death the grafting scalpel, and leadership of the club, was passed on to Serge Veronoff, who avoided experimenting on himself and chose instead to offer ageing men with too much money the chance of a lifetime: immortality in the guise of monkey testicles.

Interest in this technique was not as foolish as it now sounds; the science of endocrinology – the study of hormones – was still developing and, chronologically, gland grafting came well before the Hayflick limit had been discovered. Since it was thought that cells grown outside the body were immortal, Veronoff argued that ageing inside the body must be due to some sort of deficiency that prevented the body's cells from living forever. It had long been observed that ageing in men was associated with a corresponding failure in sexual vigour and since the worlds of both scientific endeavour and gland grafting were dominated by the male of the species, the root cause of ageing was identified as the testis. Basing his surgical rationale around this scientific misunderstanding, Veronoff thought that the best way to increase lifespan and add an extra pinch of sexual sparkle was to graft on a new testicle. Working on the basis that three should function much more efficiently than two, Veronoff took testicles from monkeys and grafted them on to grateful geriatrics. So infectious was his enthusiasm that a common feeling of the day was that 'you are only as young as your glands'. This was not a new idea invented by Veronoff: since ancient times the testis had been associated with improved sexual performance and immortality. And all sorts of potions and elixirs have been concocted using extract of testis as a starting product. However, Veronoff seems to have been the first to utilise the powers of the testis externally rather than internally.

Rejuvenation became so hip that it started to crop up as a theme in popular fiction. In the Swinging Twenties the American novelist Gertrude Atherton popularised the theme of rejuvenation in her novel *Black Oxen*. The book hit the bestseller lists and was later made into a film. The plot centred around a tale of contemporary love, with a classic Romeo and his Juliet, but the novel parts company with the Shakespearean version when Romeo discovers that Juliet is a former old-age pensioner who has had the good fortune to be rejuvenated. Gertrude Atherton is reported to have written the novel from personal experience – at least to the extent that she had undergone a rejuvenation treatment. Her rejuvenation had not involved a testis graft, but in her late fifties she had had her ovaries irradiated. No one knows if the technique improved her sex life, but we do know that she lived to the age of 91; a long way off the maximum lifespan of 135, but respectable all the same.

The apparent success of the 'Gland Grafters' also spurred novelist Bertram Gayton into writing *The Gland Stealers*. This was a much more comic version of contemporary love and indeed was so contemporary that this time Romeo was a

95-year-old would-be sexual athlete whom Veronoff transformed into a youthful sexual athlete by the addition of an
extra testicle donated by a gorilla. Impressed by his new-found
sexual vigour, Romeo insists on rejuvenating his 70-year-old
girlfriend (who is not called Jane). To demonstrate his
gratitude to Veronoff he decides to solve the surgeon's spare
part supply problem and travels to Africa in search of more
generous gorillas. Like all good morality plays this one ends
with a stern message: Romeo discovers to his horror that the
effects of rejuvenation wear off, to be replaced by accelerated
ageing.

Outside the arena of popular fiction, scientific interest in
gland grafting increased when the results of operations carried
out at San Quentin prison in California were published in the
scientific journal *Endocrinology*. Testicles removed from
executed murderers had been grafted on to other ageing
inmates. The prison doctors described the operations as successful, with the elderly recipients not only rejuvenated but
supposedly cured of other minor ailments like acne and
asthma. The results of the operations also lent credence to the
idea that three really are better than two, because at the annual
prison games one 70-year-old who had been given an extra
testicle managed to beat much younger prisoners who were
unlucky enough to be running with just the usual pair. These
experiments were to lead to a spurious ethical debate over
whether it was morally justified to extend the lifespan of a life-
sentence prisoner when he would spend his extra years inside
prison.

However, gland grafting was a technique that was to achieve
its greatest notoriety among a very different sort of clientele.
By the early 1920s, celebrities who had received gland grafts
started to come out of the operating theatre closet. This might
not have been the most welcome sort of publicity Veronoff
could have asked for because many of them tended to be actors
who were 'resting', and fading film stars who wanted to trade
their surgical gossip for a rejuvenated career, or at the very
least, cash in hand.

Working on the principle that all publicity was good publicity, Veronoff went on to make gland grafts one of the hottest
commodities of the Jazz Age since the Charleston. Members of

the orthodox scientific community chose to ignore him and so he was free to relieve large numbers of ageing males of even larger quantities of money. Testicle transplants were so popular that tales of personal rejuvenation took over from charades as the high point of entertainment at society dinner parties. 'Immortality' and 'monkey glands' became the buzzwords of the rich and famous.

Although it is now known that the testis releases a male sex hormone called testosterone which is intimately involved with the male sex drive, this hormone has never been shown to increase lifespan or to bring about rejuvenation. Even if testosterone did have the power to rejuvenate, Veronoff's testis transplants would never have worked because the body's complex defence system has been designed to search out any foreign tissue or organisms and destroy them. The fine workings of this defence system, the immune system, can mean the difference between life and death: it is so effective that it has taken years for transplant scientists to develop drugs which allow organs like human hearts and kidneys to be transplanted. The key word here is human; tissues (any cells or organs) from animals grafted into a human will ultimately be rejected, whatever drugs are given. By today's standards, Veronoff's testis grafts were very sloppy indeed; slices of the monkey tissue were attached to the outside of the patient's own testicles. Today's transplant surgeons devote hours of their time to the painstaking process whereby the blood vessels of the donor organ are joined up to those of the patient. This means that the new tissue can extract from the bloodstream the food and oxygen which is vital if the organ is to have any chance of surviving. Without such a life support system, Veronoff's glands must have just withered and died.

It has been suggested that Veronoff was not a charlatan interested purely in personal gain, but someone who genuinely believed that his gland operations did work. If this sounds a little far-fetched, bearing in mind the large sums of money involved, it is possible that without the benefit of today's modern microscopic techniques he mistook the invasion of cells from the patient's immune system into the monkey testis as meaning that his graft had 'taken'. As for the patient, the effect of the graft was nothing short of miraculous because, of course, that's what the patient wanted to believe. This was an excellent example of what is now considered to be the bane of the researcher's life and goes by the name of the 'placebo' effect. This psychological sense of well-being is so powerful that it has been known to make sugar pills as effective as real drugs and every clinical trial is now designed to overcome its influence. In those days however, shouts of 'Eureka' from apparently rejuvenated patients were enough to persuade medical salesmen and clients alike that the treatment worked.

According to David Hamilton, author of *The Monkey Gland Affair*, Veronoff was in some ways a scientific pioneer. By the mid-1980s drugs to prevent tissue rejection had become so sophisticated that medical attention once again turned to the monkey as a source of donor organs. Indeed, in 1984 a baboon heart transplanted into a human baby hit the headlines across the world and the graft, although controversial and not ultimately successful, lasted longer than was expected. Hamilton believes that Veronoff was the first to launch the debate – and face up to the criticism – over the use of animals as tissue donors for human transplants.

A renegade American member of the Gland Grafters club was an unusual character called 'Doctor' J. R. Brinkley, who reputedly bought his medical diploma from a university in Kansas and then built a clinic to get his fair share of the testicle transplant market. Unlike Veronoff, he put his money and his faith into the sexual organs of goats – and he struck gold. He made so much money out of his virile billy goats that he was able to build his own radio station with the call sign KFKB – Kansas First, Kansas Best. With no one to censor the output of his station, he used it to advertise rejuvenation in the hope of seducing the male population of Kansas into investing in the sexual attributes of the young goat and so encouraging them to pay for a transplant. The power of the media was such that many are reported to have taken up the rejuvenation option including the then Editor of the *Los Angeles Times* and the Chancellor of the Chicago Law School. It was rumoured that Brinkley's first customer had been suffering from infertility but, with a little help from a goat testis, he went on to father a boy named 'Billy'.

Brinkley's surgical methods were never published, but

whether or not his patients were rejuvenated, his bank account had never been healthier. By 1930 he was a millionaire and would have continued to amass a fortune if local doctors had not organised a campaign to expose him and his qualifications as fraudulent. Undaunted, Brinkley used the time to run for the post of Governor of Kansas and launched the sort of political campaign never seen before in the South. For once money did not talk; Brinkley may have held the key to their sexual vigour, but he failed to capture the hearts and minds of the voters. Still confident of the appeal of his virile billy goats he moved his business to Mexico, but rejuvenatory times and tastes were changing. Patients were becoming interested in something a little more sophisticated than goats' testicles.

While Brinkley's appeal was fading, the doors of the Gland Grafting club had opened to admit a new member – this time in Europe. Dr Paul Niehans started his immortality clinic in a secluded part of Montreux in Switzerland. Like the other members before him, Niehans was a charming, charismatic figure, with an added dash of mystery. The son of a well-known Swiss doctor and a German mother, he was rumoured to be the nephew of no less a figure than Kaiser Wilhelm of Germany.

While Niehans had been setting up his clinic, the field of endocrinology had been growing up fast and was now beginning to flex its academic muscles. After a long period of scepticism, scientific attitudes towards gland grafting were becoming more sympathetic because of the discovery of certain key gland secretions. Hormones extracted from the thyroid gland and insulin secreted by the pancreas had been shown to produce remarkable effects. Insulin had already been shown to have the power to revive diabetic patients from coma and return them to normal health. There was every reason to believe that testis grafts should be able to rejuvenate the parts that other hormones could not reach.

In 1927, when it was discovered that the pituitary gland was the master gland in the body, controlling all the body's hormones, Niehans focused his attention on the pituitary. Using pituitary glands taken from cows or sheep he transplanted them into patients in the hope of curing diabetes and rheumatism. He also believed his pituitary gland transplants would cause a growth spurt in dwarfs and quoted a height increase of 0.32 metres after one of his injections with cells taken from a young calf. This work added to his fame: when he travelled to America shortly after these experiments he was apparently mobbed by large numbers of people of small stature.

Gland grafting was now such a topic of conversation among the elite that even Noël Coward could not resist including it in the dialogue of the play *Private Lives*:
'Elyot: Would you be young always? If you could choose?'
Amanda: No, I don't think so, not if it meant having awful bull's glands popped into me . . .'

The following year in Lausanne a young woman was to make gland grafting history. She was undergoing an operation for an overactive thyroid gland when the surgeon accidentally cut through the parathyroid glands, which lie next to the thyroid. This caused a form of tetanus in which the muscles went into spasm. By the time Niehans was consulted the muscle contractions had increased to a near-fatal level. Unable to repair the damage, he injected a solution of parathyroid glands taken from a young calf. The results were amazing. The patient not only made a full recovery, but went on to live in perfect health for the next 30 years. The European version of gland grafting had come of age and Paul Niehans had been elevated to star status.

When gland grafting went out of vogue in the 1930s, Niehans concentrated on the injection of cells. This new rejuvenation technique was called 'cell therapy' and was based on Veronoff's hypothesis that ageing was due to a deficiency in the glands.

A cloud of secrecy surrounded the technique but it is clear that it was based on cells taken from various parts of sheep embryos. This rather bizarre experimental technique seems to have developed from the idea popular at the time that cells taken from an unborn animal would not be rejected by the human body. The choice of an unborn lamb for donor organs seems rather arbitrary, but might have been due to ease of supply or, more colourfully, it has been suggested that Niehans may have exploited the ancient idea that the lamb was an animal that could bestow magical properties on those who drank its blood, or perhaps were injected with its cells.

Drinking lamb's blood might have been a more successful route to rejuvenation because it is now thought that any lamb cells injected into the body would have been destroyed by the immune system within minutes. However, at that time there was no scientific evidence to dispute the claims for cell therapy, which continued to attract the rich and famous.

Even if there had been concerted scientific opposition to Niehans' work, it would probably have had little effect on the ageing consumer. The failure to publish controlled clinical trials had not stopped people opting for gland grafts in the past and cell therapy was to prove no different. Throughout his lifetime Niehans' operating lists were to read like a copy of *Who's Who*, always liberally sprinkled with the very rich and the very famous.

Unlike Brinkley, Niehans had no need to resort to advertising on radio: his good looks and lavish lifestyle created the necessary aura of success. Around this framework of interest there was a sense of mystery and intrigue which was an added bait for potential customers. All paying visitors to the Swiss clinic were guaranteed anonymity. Inquisitive gossip columnists and hardened journalists tried every trick in the book to find out who among the rich and famous had beaten a path to immortality on the shores of Lake Geneva. Gloria Swanson and Somerset Maugham talked openly about their visits, but Charlie Chaplin went to the court when a newspaper suggested that he had visited the clinic for rejuvenation treatment. Noël Coward paid a short visit, but whether for treatment or to gather material for his plays is unclear. At one time it was even rumoured in the gossip columns that the Duke and Duchess of Windsor were residents at the clinic and Niehans' protestations that this was not the case only served to increase the interest.

What finally brought success to Niehans' door was not the activity of the media but the awesome power of personal testimony: once injected with sheep's cells, patients claimed to feel years younger. Having paid dearly for the privilege, it is not surprising that the placebo effect was alive and well and encouraging extravagant reports of success. Glowing testimonies were not confined to one side of the sexual divide; men talked of regaining sexual potency, women of losing the symptoms of the menopause. They reported looking and feeling years younger. Niehans, they were convinced, had raided the lost Ark and had come out clutching the elixir of youth.

Niehans' greatest hour came in 1953 when he was rushed to the bedside of Pope Pius XII, then in very poor health. No doubt eyebrows were raised at the Customs point when Niehans arrived in Rome with two pregnant ewes. Jetlag obviously had no detrimental effect on the animals because therapy using cells taken from their unborn lambs seemed to cure the Pope almost overnight. On his recovery the Pope was so grateful he awarded Niehans the Pontifical College chair vacated by Alexander Fleming. This was a major scientific honour and was deemed to be such a controversial decision that it led to a new constitution being proposed for the Pontifical Academy, the Vatican's select group of scientists.

In spite of the controversy, this was the sort of publicity that money couldn't buy. Niehans retired from active participation in his clinic in 1965 a rich man, and died six years later at the age of 88 – well past the usual three-score years and ten, but cell-therapy – assuming he had used it on himself – had obviously not allowed him to extend his maximum lifespan.

However, his clinic and cell therapy live on. Rejuvenation is still big business and specially bred black sheep are the raw material of an industry once described as Switzerland's most profitable tourist venture. Each week the ageing hopefuls arrive at the clinic under conditions of strict secrecy, ready to receive an exotic cell cocktail. Every week at least one of the pregnant black sheep is 'sacrificed' and the unborn lamb taken from the womb. Each organ is placed in a labelled dish while the patients wait in their private rooms. Every usable part of the foetus is carefully removed and labelled. A tailor-made solution containing a mixture of cells is then sucked into a syringe and each patient receives six to twelve syringes of the potion. Then comes the undignified part of the procedure, when all of this fluid is injected into the body via a large muscle, usually the backside – but then no one ever said the search for immortality would be painless.

What even the most generous of scientists find hard to accept is the claim that the body's immune system will not recognise the cells from the unborn lamb as foreign and so set off the normal process of rejection. It is true that while growing in the womb cells from the embryo do not have the characteristic markers by which the cells in the immune system would normally classify them as friend or foe. Even so, most scientists believe that if the lamb cells were not rejected out of hand by the immune system they would be broken down before they could exert a beneficial effect.

Another unconfirmed scientific claim which doctors using cell therapy continue to make is that injected embryo cells migrate towards a related organ or tissue. So, for example, patients with ageing hearts are given cells from the heart of the unborn lamb; in the same way patients with kidney or liver disease are injected with cells from these specific organs, while impotence requires the injection of cells from the sexual organs of the lamb embryo. To produce complete rejuvenation a mixture of cells from different organs is prescribed, consisting mainly of cells from the endocrine glands. The idea behind this specificity is that cells from the unborn lamb will home in on the defective tissue and rejuvenate it. Most scientists find it difficult to understand why a cell from a particular part of a lamb embryo should home in on its human equivalent. Furthermore they point out that when young cells are added to old cells in laboratory culture, there is no rejuvenation effect, and all the cells continue to be governed by their individual Hayflick limits.

We will see in Chapter Five that brain tissue grafted from a human embryo can rejuvenate patients with the degenerative brain condition Parkinson's disease, but in this case the transplant is from human to human, so the rejection problems are reduced, and the cells are actually placed at the site of damage in the brain, not injected into the backside in the hope that they might somehow find their way to the place where they are needed.

Although 'personal testimonials' and many European studies have reported miraculous effects, no hard scientific data has been presented to substantiate the value of cell therapy as a rejuvenation treatment rather than just another (if highly expensive) version of the placebo effect. As more and more scientists take up research in the field of ageing, the clinic has found itself under increasing attack.

To combat its critics, the clinic decided to appoint a figure as glamorous and as charismatic as Niehans himself, Christiaan Barnard. Barnard, the first man to carry out a heart transplant, joined the clinic as an honorary member of the medical team. He said he would undertake research work into the field of cell transplantation from his base at the University of Cape Town and so determine whether cell therapy had any effect. When he was appointed he said, 'We can see the life of any cell by growing it in a culture and observing the number of times it multiplies before it dies. If we then add foetal lamb cells to it and observe that it multiplies more than the set number of times it is genetically supposed to do, then we have shown that foetal lamb cells actually do revive the life of the human cell.' He has since appeared to challenge the view that the foetal cells perform a mystical rejuvenation act and instead claims that the lamb cells work by releasing substances, possibly extra genetic material like DNA, which may increase the life of the ageing cells. At the time of writing no scientific papers explaining this viewpoint have been published in any recognised journal.

What is even more confusing is that the original clinic started by Niehans now seems to compete with the Clinique Paul Niehans, just down the road in Vevy, Switzerland. Founded by Niehans' daughter Coralie, this clinic doesn't use specially bred black sheep but instead imports cells from Dr Joachim Stein, one of the leading practitioners of cell therapy in West Germany. Since 1954 Stein has exported the lyophilized (freeze-dried) version of fresh cells taken from approximately 70 different tissues, including testis, placenta, heart, liver, spleen, kidney, bone marrow and brain. Up to 3,000 specially bred sheep are kept in isolation on a site near the university city of Heidelberg. Apparently, each sheep is numbered and has its own individual medical record, and, as in the Swiss clinic, ewes are delivered of their lambs in an abbatoir by having their wombs removed with the foetus inside. The required organs are removed, sliced and deep frozen. Tiny pieces of each organ are then freeze-dried, and placed in ampoules.

Whatever the legal situation in Europe, the therapeutic

claims for cell therapy have never been recognised in the United States where it is illegal to practise it. The Americans also have more stringent rules governing the importation of drugs and other clinical materials and will not allow the cells to be imported. This has probably not interfered with the international sales of freeze-dried cells since the laboratories in Switzerland and Germany are able legitimately to export their products via Mexico and the Bahamas. From these countries they can be legally shipped to the United States.

The situation is very different in Britain, where charm and charisma are sometimes not as influential as a Harley Street address. Close to this hallowed street Therapeutic Immunology or TI is on offer. This is a form of cell therapy but it differs from the Swiss variety in that only the genetic material of young cells is injected into the patient. Like the Swiss treatment it is expensive, but it still attracts its share of the monied members of the British public.

In Chapter Two we saw that one of the major theories of ageing, the Error Theory, involves the incorporation of errors into proteins, particularly those proteins which are the enzymes designed to replace and repair any damage to the DNA. According to this Error Theory, if too many of these faulty proteins accumulate in the cell, an 'error catastrophe' will occur and the cell will die. Therapeutic Immunology claims to provide an antidote to this form of ageing by injecting new genetic material which will replace the damaged nucleic acids like DNA in the ageing cells, and boost the formation of new, error-free proteins. However the doubts of many scientists about the efficacy of this technique will only be removed when the results of clinical trials are published. At the time of writing this has not happened.

In Germany there is already a well-established tradition of using genetic material extracted from different organs of animals. As in cell therapy, it is hoped that the nucleic acid from a particular sheep organ will rejuvenate the same organ in the person to whom it is given. One of the best-known nucleic acid concoctions is called Regenerensen or RN-13. It seems to be a sort of casserole made according to a complex recipe that includes material from testes, ovaries, placenta, hypothalamus, adrenals, liver, pituitary and spleen, together with a dash of brain and kidney.

Some would-be rejuvenators have suggested that nucleic acid therapy could work just as easily if it were simply eaten rather than injected. One of the more colourful proponents of this dietary theory was Dr Benjamin Frank. For 25 years the New York doctor investigated the use of genetic material in the treatment of ageing, but it wasn't until 1977 that his work came under scientific scrutiny when he shot to fame after writing *Dr Frank's No Ageing Diet*. The book made the bestseller lists, but academics were not impressed.

According to Frank ageing is not due to the production of damaged or faulty DNA brought about by the build-up of errors, but instead comes about because of the inability of the cell to synthesise enough normal DNA to meet its needs as it gets older. For Frank the obvious remedy was to boost the amount of DNA available to the cell by adding it to the diet. To achieve this his ideal anti-ageing formula contains nucleic acids combined with vitamins, minerals, amino acids and some sugars. The end result is meant to be little short of rejuvenation.

Frank's claims are certainly controversial and they have been attacked by orthodox scientists as being untested and unsubstantiated. Why he never published any of the results of his animal experiments or a report on the effects of genetic material on his many thousands of patients is not known, but it does affect his credibility. Since his dietary regime was based on his own subjective evaluation of the results, it leaves the way open for bias and the insidious workings of the placebo effect.

Scientifically, 'Frank's No Ageing Diet' is also difficult to swallow because his nucleic acids are taken by mouth, and like any other food will be broken down in the stomach by digestive enzymes and will never get the chance to pass on the 'youthful' information locked inside the DNA. To add to all this, the anti-ageing effects of all nucleic acid treatments have yet to be proven, regardless of how they are administered.

The second part of the Therapeutic Immunology technique is even more baffling to the scientific authorities. According to David Abbot, author of *New Life for Old*, antibodies originally produced inside a horse are given to the ageing patient in the form of suppositories. Again Switzerland plays a major part in the whole process, because the antibodies are imported weekly from a laboratory there.

Antibodies are produced by our body's defence system in response to the invasion of substances that it recognizes as foreign. The immune system decides whether a cell is friendly or foreign via small, characteristic proteins on the cell's surface called antigens. These antigens act like fingerprints, so that when the immune system's defence cells police the body they can check a cell's 'fingerprints' against known invaders and either pass them or make antibodies to destroy them. For every new antigen the defence system encounters, it produces a corresponding antibody which destroys the foe. This method of functioning is common to the immune systems of all animals. In order to get the defence cells of the horse to produce antibodies, cells with foreign antigens must be injected. These usually come in the form of a cell cocktail from the foetus of another animal. This in itself is confusing because the justification for using unborn lambs in cell therapy is that their cells have not yet developed antigens and so cannot be recognised by the defence systems as being foreign.

As in cell therapy the organs in the foetus are carefully dissected out. Each horse is then injected with a cell extract taken from one organ so that each horse is kept for each organ. So, for example, a horse which is injected with extract of heart will be injected only with this extract for the rest of its working life.

Although its supporters had described Therapeutic Immunology as a vaccination against growing old, horse antibodies have been recommended for an amazing cornucopia of disorders including sexual impotence. In the quest for immortality, breathing new life into a dead or dying sex life seems to be uppermost in everyone's minds.

To answer their needs, and fill a very lucrative gap in the anti-ageing market, a specific product has been developed which is claimed to put some sparkle back into a less-than-perfect sex life and just in case any ageing studs were in doubt about its proposed effects, it has been named Bio-erectile. Despite the sexist title, there are two types of bio-erectile treatments, one for men and one for women. The male elixir,

Bio-erectile M, contains antibodies derived from the testicles, while Bio-erectile F has antibodies from the ovary and is designed for the menopausal woman.

The name of the product may instil confidence in its users, but from a strictly clinical point of view it is difficult to see how horse antibodies could achieve the desired effect. Antibodies are very large molecules, and it is impossible for them to be absorbed into the bloodstream from the rectum when given as suppositories. Until scientific evidence is published supporting its action, any claims from born-again Casanovas must be psychological and be put down to the placebo effect, around which most of the successes of the rejuvenation business seem to revolve.

Sexual activity has been linked with longevity since time immemorial and it has even been suggested that sexual practice itself can be used to increase the lifespan. Followers of the ancient Taoist religion were of the opposite opinion, and thought that the process of ejaculation shortened one's life because some important essence or 'ching' was lost with the seminal fluid. This belief is common to many cultures and religions and is one of the reasons why masturbation is often thought to be weakening. However, the Taoists themselves considered celibacy to be abnormal and preferred sexual intercourse without ejaculation, which allowed them to experience the pleasures of the flesh without sacrificing their 'ching'.

Paradoxically, in many cultures sexual potency is associated with renewed youth, and for thousands of years people have tried to maintain this potency throughout their lives; for instance, the placenta, testis and semen of young animals all have roles to play in traditional Chinese medicine.

In many ways modern medicine has carried on the tradition by balancing out hormone deficiencies in men and women with artificial male and female sex hormones. Male impotence is treated with testosterone, the sex hormone made in the testis and the modern-day version of Brown-Séquard's testicular graft. It is ironic to think that both Veronoff and Brown-Séquard were correct in predicting that failing sexual vigour in men was due to the reduction of some vital substance; that substance was testosterone. However, while this sort of hormone treatment can cure certain types of impotence, the Gland Grafters were wrong to think that sex hormones were the answer to an ageing mind and body. Even the improvement in sexual vigour brought about by testosterone can sometimes be short lived. The same may even be true of hormone therapy given to women after the menopause. This treatment is based on replacing the female hormone oestrogen, which declines rapidly when the ovary shuts down hormone production at the menopause. As well as relieving the uncomfortable side effects of oestrogen loss like joint pain, breast pain and swelling, some women say it makes them feel rejuvenated. Full-blown rejuvenation is hard to verify, but there have been reports of improved complexion, and a reversal of osteoporosis or brittle bones. Hormone Replacement Therapy has so far been successful although, since it has only been used for a relatively short time, its long-term effects on the body have yet to be discovered.

Hormones are not just important in sustaining our interest in sex; they are also vital for everyday health and well-being. When any of the glands produce too much or too little hormone, the results can be devastating. For this reason it is now accepted that the workings of the various glands, particularly the pituitary gland, can determine the speed at which we age. This being the case, there was tremendous excitement when American scientists announced that a hormone produced by the adrenal gland appeared to increase the maximum lifespan of mice.

   This hormone, called dehydroepiandrosterone or DHEA, is the most abundant of all the hormones made by the adrenal gland, but no one has ever discovered just exactly what its role is. Arthur Schwartz at Temple University in the United States became interested in DHEA when his research team uncovered research carried out over 30 years ago which showed that large amounts of DHEA were secreted by the adrenal gland up to the age of 25, after which production of the hormone started to dwindle. Later research discovered that levels of DHEA were high in unborn babies, declined to almost zero after birth and then rose sharply at puberty. By the age of 70 the hormone was barely detectable. These results were more than just intriguing; such an extreme decline was unheard of among adrenal hormones.

The plot thickened when a series of articles highlighting the work of British scientists was published in the early 1970s. This gave the results of a long-term investigation into breast cancer carried out by the Imperial Cancer Research Fund in London. One of the most striking findings of the study was the fact that DHEA was abnormally low in women who already had breast cancer or who would go on to develop the disease. The ICRF measured the amounts of three hormones, including DHEA, in the urine of women aged between 29 and 60. Of the women who later developed cancer of the ovary, the levels of all three hormones were very low. The results were most striking for DHEA. It is always difficult to unravel cause and effect in cancer but, if the absence of DHEA was linked to the incidence of cancer, Schwartz argued that its presence might prevent it developing.

Then in 1977 it was found that DHEA fed to genetically obese mice would cause them to lose weight. Initially critics argued that this result was due to DHEA suppressing the appetite of the mice, but it was soon shown that the rodent slimmers ate just as much laboratory fodder as their fat friends.

The evidence was mounting that DHEA was able to prevent cancer and cure obesity, at least in mice and rats, but the precise way in which it produced these results remained a mystery. DHEA did not behave like other hormones and did not seem to be stored in the adrenal glands; as soon as it was made it was released into the bloodstream. The issue was further complicated by the way DHEA was used in the body as a raw material for the manufacture of sex hormones, even though the comparatively vast quantities of DHEA released by the adrenal gland would hardly be needed solely for their production.

This intimate link with the sex hormones was to prove a scientific red herring for many years, and interfered with the determination of whatever therapeutic effects DHEA may or may not have had; in Europe, DHEA was prescribed for a whole host of conditions, including osteoporosis, depression, high blood pressure and the menopause. In almost every case any improvements were put down to the conversion of DHEA into male and female sex hormones somewhere in the body.

Despite this confusion, Arthur Schwartz noticed that his overweight rats not only lost weight when they were given DHEA, they also looked much younger; their bodies were sleek and the colour of their fur remained youthful. DHEA appeared to have an anti-ageing effect. This observation was confirmed when it was announced that DHEA had increased the maximum lifespan of certain strains of mice.

However, many scientists – particularly in the UK – adopt a jaundiced attitude towards the rejuvenatory properties of DHEA. At best they reluctantly accept that DHEA may have an anti-obesity effect – at least in overweight rats! So, it seems unlikely that the path to immortality will end at a door marked DHEA but if you remain unconvinced, a word of scientific caution: the initial experiments only demonstrated an increase in the lifespan of rats bred to live for a short time and the effect of DHEA on the longevity of long-lived mice has yet to be decided. Even more worrying is the discovery that DHEA given to mice for long periods of time causes tumours of the pituitary gland. Safer, synthetic versions of the compound are now being tested, but it is unlikely that the DHEA version of everlasting youth will find its way on to the shelves for at least another 10 years.

The American Food and Drug Administration has however already had to remove DHEA from unscrupulous health food stores where it was being sold as an anti-obesity remedy. But this sort of action will not deter the pro-longevity movement. In chemists, drug stores and health food shops all over Britain and the USA rejuvenation is at the top of everyone's shopping list, and millions are spent on vitamins and food supplements which are claimed to preserve youth and delay the onset of ageing. One of the most sought after is Gerovital, which has been at the centre of scientific controversy for almost three decades.

It was first discovered as a so-called anti-ageing potion in 1945 by a Rumanian physician Ana Aslan but its main ingredient, procaine, has a history strangely interwoven with the early practitioners of psychoanalysis. When Freud and his colleagues first used cocaine, they were unaware that this effective local anaesthetic was also addictive. When procaine

was synthesised, the problems were solved. It could anaes-
thetise nerves in the areas where it was injected, yet within a
few moments it was broken down and the nerves were able to
return to their normal state. It was non-addictive and
non-toxic.

A short time after procaine was discovered, it was realised
that as well as numbing the nerves, it also relieved the pain of
arthritis. However, procaine was to be elevated to even loftier
heights. During World War Two, a Rumanian professor and
his assistant, Ana Aslan, found that patients who were receiving procaine injections claimed to feel younger and healthier,
and some, like the rats taking DHEA, had their hair colour
restored. Wasting no time and acting on these observations,
Ana Aslan opened a clinic in Rumania and proceeded to offer
treatments for diseases including arthritis and asthma.
However, her therapeutic *pièce de résistance* was a procaine
preparation called Gerovital which could apparently banish
the symptoms of ageing and return its users to former levels of
youth and beauty. The advertising must have been successful
because for the last 30 years Aslan has used Gerovital to treat
patients at the National Institute of Gerontology and
Geriatrics in Bucharest and there are many personal
testimonials to prove its effectiveness. The rich and
rejuvenated are reputed to include John F. Kennedy, Marlene
Dietrich, Charles de Gaulle and Somerset Maugham, although
none of these have talked openly about their rejuvenation
treatment.

In order to be able to use procaine in this way, Aslan had to
circumvent the very properties that made it useful as a local
anaesthetic. Procaine's numbing effects on the nerves are very
short lived because it is rapidly broken down to para-
aminobenzoic acid (PABA) and diethylaminoethanol
(DEAE). To try to stabilise her anti-ageing formula, Aslan
added two chemicals; benzoic acid and metabisulfite. Even so,
orthodox medicine was not impressed. An editorial appeared
in the *British Medical Journal* at the height of interest in
procaine which argued that, although it was an effective
anaesthetic and a useful anti-arthritic drug, there was no
evidence that it could affect the ageing process. This pessimistic
approach was reinforced by a series of trials in the UK using

elderly patients suffering from dementia. Gerovital was found to have no effect and most doctors thought that would be the last they would hear of Ana Aslan or her ageing remedy. They had underestimated the devotion of its followers and the power of the wish to be forever young. Its popularity grew and grew.

Aslan's customers were unmoved by the scientific evidence which proved the only consistent effect of Gerovital was as a mild anti-depressant, which might explain the subjective reports of feeling younger and better about old age.

While Aslan and her research team have reported that Gerovital increases the maximum lifespan of rats, other studies have not confirmed this effect on longevity. It is not easy to disprove all the claims that are made for it, but it is equally difficult to find scientific evidence to support those claims. So it seems the advice on Gerovital has to be DON'T keep taking the tablets.

It now seems that Gerovital has lost out in the anti-ageing popularity stakes to the more fashionable ginseng. Unlike Gerovital, no one manufactured ginseng; it grows naturally in China and Korea. The virtues of ginseng in the battle against ageing have been proclaimed in China for thousands of years. Today ginseng has found its way on to the shelves of health food shops across the western world.

Botanically speaking ginseng is the root of a perennial herb (*Panax Ginseng*) which grows in the damp mountain forests of Eastern Asia. According to ginseng snobs the best variety is found in Korea, but other strains grow in limited areas of China, Russia, Japan and the USA. Originally it was gathered in China by special ginseng-searchers appointed by the Emperors of the Han dynasty to perform the same function carried out by the truffle-hunting pigs of Europe. Successful sightings of the scarce root were rewarded with gold and silver, but the Chinese are a demanding lot, and not to be fooled with, for any adulteration of the precious root was punishable by death.

Today ginseng collecting has got a little out of hand and the wild form of the plant is now extremely rare, increasing its value. It has been reported that in China, the price of the wild root depends on two factors: the age of the root, which can be judged by the wrinkles on its neck and the age of the buyer. To artificially cultivate ginseng, man had to recreate the natural conditions it needs. Four-foot wide straw panels are erected over the crop to act like the natural forest, protecting the plant from torrential rain and hot sun. It takes seven years to grow, and draws so much from the soil that the land must lie fallow for 15 years afterwards. Not surprisingly cultivated ginseng is the most expensive root in the world, costing over 50,000 dollars per ton, and like all the other elixirs, no self-respecting member of the rich and famous would be without it. It is rumoured to have reached the important parts of Mao Tse-tung and most of the Russian Cosmonaut crew.

Scientifically it is important to find out whether ginseng has any measurable effect or whether, like many of the other elixirs, it can claim its success on the coat-tails of the placebo effect. To test the effect of ginseng a London firm called Consultax Labs carried out some experiments in 1974 on swimming mice. The mice were given different doses of ginseng for two to four weeks, then were encouraged to swim until they were exhausted. It was found that mice given ginseng could swim longer before becoming exhausted. So far as mice are concerned, they can withstand fatigue better when they had ginseng, but it's hard to relate these results to humans. While these results are interesting, they were supplied by the manufacturer of the product.

During prolonged exercise fatigue happens when energy stored in the body in the form of glycogen in muscles and the liver is used up. But if the animal is able to produce substances called fatty acids, then these can be used instead of glycogen and the point of fatigue can be delayed. Tests done at the human performance centre in Oregon – again using mice – seemed to show that the animals given ginseng used their fatty acid stores first, before the glycogen, allowing them to swim for longer periods. How ginseng achieves this effect is not known, but its exact mode of action is of no interest to budding athletes, keen to prevent fatigue and compete longer. They seem suitably impressed; Britain's top racing cyclists used a ginseng-based capsule as part of their preparations for the 1980 Olympic games. The decision was taken after a cycling team taking ginseng during the Montreal games returned with a bronze medal.

Ginseng has also been claimed to fight stress and tension. To explain this effect Dr Stephen Fulder has suggested that ginseng stimulates the adrenal gland to produce a hormone that helps us to fight stress. Dr Fulder, author of *An End to Ageing*, cites the results of experiments conducted at the Maudsley Hospital in London using nurses who regularly change their working shift patterns from day to night. To take into account the placebo effect the nurses did not know whether they were receiving ginseng or a dummy pill, and then their mood, performance and tiredness were assessed as they went about their duties. Small quantities of ginseng given for three days seemed to improve these rather subjective measurements.

Dr Fulder is a firm believer in ginseng and attributes nearly all of its effects to an ability to protect the body from the damage caused by stress. While many of his scientific papers concentrate on the fine detail of blood supply, sugar supply, liver function, improvements in cholesterol levels and so on, most of these effects are largely explained by a proposed effect on the stress hormones released by the adrenal glands.

Since the adrenal glands are themselves controlled by the pituitary and hypothalamus which produce the master hormones in the body's stress control system, Dr Fulder decided to test the effects of ginseng on these areas of the brain. Animals were given small amounts of a stress hormone which had a radioactive label attached. After ginseng was administered, certain areas of the brain, like the hypothalamus, were even more sensitive to the stress hormone. Dr Fulder thinks this might explain why people would feel better and more alert after taking ginseng; furthermore, they would be better at dealing with stress. He argues that because stress is often associated with disease, a resistance to stress would improve resistance to disease.

Whether ginseng really does work on the brain in this manner has not been confirmed, but there can be no doubt that a large part of its commercial success must be at least partly due to its reputed ability to rekindle or increase sexual potency. Ginseng is reported to have kept Henry Kissinger tired but smiling on his honeymoon. The Chinese attribute this to the fact that nature consists of a balance of yin (female) and yang (male) forces. The sexual rejuvenation business is heavily biased towards the male since ginseng is meant to pep up your yang, and is a sort of vegetarian version of Veronoff's testicle transplant.

However, one research team found that it had a moistening effect on the membrane of the vagina in menopausal women, an action similar to that of the female hormone; an obvious effect on the yin, not the yang. This effect of ginseng is now acknowledged and preparations of the Chinese remedy are thought to contain small quantities of oestradiol and oestrone, substances which behave like female sex hormones in the body. This might explain why doctors at the Royal Marsden Hospital in London noticed swelling of the breasts and enlarging of the nipples in women who had been taking ginseng. The Royal Marsden is a leading cancer hospital and visitors had given ginseng to female cancer patients because of its alleged anti-cancer properties. This ability to produce such odd side effects is one reason why doctors are not happy about ginseng being used indiscriminately; many of them feel that ginseng ought to be covered by the same rules that govern medicines. Drug or no drug, it can still be abused. American scientists estimate that some five to six million Americans have turned to ginseng in the form of roots, teas and tablets. It is even sold in certain types of fizzy drink. It does have an effect as a stimulant but in high doses it produces what is now called the 'ginseng abuse syndrome'; high blood pressure, nervousness, and diarrhoea – far from the publicised joys of a healthy old age.

As for the 64-million dollar question: will it prolong life? The answer is a resounding scientific 'no' according to a study at Chelsea College in London. Mice were divided into three groups; one was given ginseng from the age of eight weeks until the end of their lifespan, the second group was given ginseng from 52 weeks of age until death, and the third group was left untreated. The amount of ginseng given was carefully estimated to approach a normal human dose. All three groups of mice lived for the same length of time; it would appear that ginseng does not prolong maximum lifespan.

If the process of ageing can be thought of as a combination of a genetic programme and general wear and tear, then many scientists believe it ought to be possible to devise ways to protect the cells from this sort of damage and prolong life. This logic has led to many people dosing themselves with concoctions of vitamins and other anti-oxidants in an attempt to protect themselves.

In Chapter Two we heard how some scientists believe that highly reactive molecules called free radicals are responsible for the damage to our cells that ultimately ends in ageing. Free radicals are formed in the body as a byproduct of breathing oxygen but to combat their effects all human cells contain biological defence mechanisms in the form of enzymes and some vitamins that neutralise their effects. As we get older these defence mechanisms are thought to slow down or act less efficiently so that damage becomes uncontrolled. Since part of our anti-oxidant defences include vitamins from the diet, at least one American scientist believes that if we get the doses right, then vitamins could help us to stay young. Dr Michael Colgan, Director of the Colgan Institute in California, thinks that eating more vitamins could increase the amount of anti-oxidants in our cells.

Dr Colgan believes that if an anti-oxidant preparation containing vitamins C and E and selenium is taken over a number of years it would be enough to prevent damage by free radicals and inhibit the development of cancer. Confident claims have been made that after eight years people who have adopted the programme and remain on it won't show signs of ageing that are apparent in their peers.

The move towards self-dosing with vitamins appears to go hand in hand with the new public awareness of health issues, but is greeted with scepticism by most of the medical establishment. They tend to adopt a conservative approach and insist that a balanced diet should contain all the vitamins and minerals we need, except in the case of babies, pregnant women, the elderly and heavy drinkers, whose bodies are less able to absorb and utilise some of the vitamins which are vital for healthy cell turnover and breakdown of alcohol by the liver. Unfortunately, as we shall discover in Chapter Seven, a balanced diet is not that easy to achieve.

A favourite transatlantic gibe is that Americans already

excrete the most expensive urine in the world, spending up to two billion dollars a year on megadoses of vitamin and mineral preparations which prop up the shelves of every drug store in the country. Dr Colgan agrees that the haphazard swallowing of large doses of vitamins and minerals is not a good idea, but he strongly disagrees that our diets contain all the vitamins we need. He points to tests that show the vitamin content of lettuces can be almost completely destroyed after a soil-to-sale life of just 48 hours; the amount of vitamin C in oranges can vary enormously depending on where the oranges were grown. Thoroughbred horses and pedigree cats and dogs are better fed than their owners, according to Colgan, because their food is carefully supplemented.

Scientifically, many of Colgan's successes with his own supplementation programme are difficult to prove or disprove since there are important gaps in the amount of information we have about vitamins. We know that when free radicals are formed outside the body in a test tube, vitamins and other anti-oxidants mop them up but we do not know if this process goes on in the body, although there is encouraging evidence about the anti-oxidant vitamin E.

When it was first discovered, vitamin E was hailed as the 'sex vitamin' because it improved the sex life of the laboratory rat. This was a claim that was never taken seriously by the medical profession, but some recent research does suggest that vitamin E might neutralise the excessive release of free radicals from defective sperm and help some infertile couples.

It has also been discovered that vitamin E can be used in the body to protect our nerves from free radical damage. Because of an inherited disorder some children are unable to absorb vitamin E; their blood lacks the proteins that carry particles of fat from the stomach to the rest of the body where they are needed. Since these proteins also carry vitamin E around the body, without them the vitamin just stays in the stomach and the nerves degenerate. This damage to the nerves is caused by free radicals which attack the outer protective membrane. Because they only have one electron, the free radicals are able to pull off hydrogen atoms weakly attached to the outside of the nerve membrane. Eventually the membrane breaks down, exposing the nerve underneath and causing crippling symptoms. According to the research team at London's Institute of Child Health, vitamin E has been ideally designed to protect the membrane; it fits snugly into the gaps in the structure, making it harder for the free radicals to get at the vulnerable hydrogen atoms. More importantly, it seems the top of the vitamin E molecule can disarm any roving free radical by sacrificing one of its own hydrogen atoms, so neutralising the free radical before it can attack any exposed part of the membrane. As well as working in theory this system also works in practice. If a child suffering from the genetic disorder is given large doses of vitamin E while still young, most of the nerve damage can be reversed.

As we saw in Chapter Two, there is also evidence that once vitamin E has donated a hydrogen atom to the free radical molecule it could be replaced by another hydrogen atom donated from vitamin C. Of course extending the argument to say that this system breaks down in ageing and that supplementing our diet with vitamins E and C will prolong our lifespan is in scientific terms a quantum leap.

The controversy over whether vitamin C does in fact prevent ageing has reached fever pitch among scientists and health food buffs on both sides of the Atlantic. Vitamin C came into the limelight in the late sixties and early seventies, when it was considered the ultimate panacea. It had been known for some time that too little vitamin C in the diet causes scurvy, a disease characterised by depression and rapid exhaustion. The gums ulcerate, the teeth drop out and blood is released into the muscles, making the victim look bruised. Not surprisingly, this eventually ends in kidney failure and death.

The effects of scurvy among sailors were terrible. Their diet consisted largely of dry biscuits and salted meat with no provision for fresh fruit or vegetables. This severe lack of vitamin C caused the death of many of the early travellers. When Vasco da Gama spent nearly a year at sea discovering the route around Africa to India in the late fifteenth century, 100 of his 160 crew fell victim to scurvy. The idea that scurvy could be prevented by a diet rich in fresh vegetables and fruit developed slowly. Finally in 1747 the Scottish physician James Lind carried out a classic experiment on sailors in the British Royal

Navy. All of his 12 subjects were already suffering from the effects of scurvy, so the idea of the experiment was to see if vitamin C could make any of them better. Two sailors were given vitamin C in the form of oranges and lemons while the remainder were treated with an assortment of cider, vinegar, sea water and sulphuric acid! Only the sailors who had been given the citrus fruits were able to overcome their scurvy while the others were still suffering. However, even scientific results as clear cut as these had no immediate effect on the bureaucrats in the British Navy. It was to take the Admiralty over 40 years to recognise the importance of Lind's work and order a daily ration of lime juice for sailors.

The sort of vitamin C deficiency that normally leads to scurvy can be cured by very small doses of the vitamin, but whether or not the sort of megadoses in the range of one to ten grams advocated by Nobel prize winner Linus Pauling can extend maximum lifespan is debatable. Pauling claims that such doses of vitamin C can extend your life and years of well-being by 25 or even 35 years and bases his beliefs on the effects of vitamins in animals. So far there has been no study which confirms the benefit he claims. He attributes this lack of hard data to the fact that it is easier to obtain reliable information about the health of guinea pigs and monkeys than of human beings, an idea reinforced by the United States Committee on the Feeding Of Laboratory Animals which recommends more vitamin C for monkeys than the US Food and Nutrition Board recommends for human beings. The effect on lifespan is still very unclear; very large doses of vitamin C were found to decrease the average lifespan of guinea pigs and fruit flies while in a recent study average lifespan was increased in mice.

In the USA it is believed that as many as 50 per cent of all adults are now consuming vitamin supplements, but so far there is little conclusive evidence to support their anti-ageing properties. The most positive approach is to say that these preparations might ensure a healthy old age but they are nowhere near being candidates for increasing longevity.

Selenium is not a vitamin but a mineral that is thought to act like an anti-oxidant in the body because it is a component of one of the anti-free radical enzymes called glutathione peroxidase. This enzyme forms the second line of defence and will mop up any free radicals that slip past vitamin E in the cell membrane. It is a rare element which is essential in trace amounts but is highly toxic in larger quantities. For many years selenium was thought to be a poison and a carcinogen. Its protective effects only came to light when a study involving 45,000 Chinese showed that a particular type of heart disease called Keshan disease was related to the concentration of selenium in the soil. Symptoms of the disease include an enlarged heart, fast pulse and low blood pressure. Where selenium in the soil was low, Keshan disease was common.

Most fruit and vegetables are quite low in selenium, although broccoli, cabbage, celery, cucumbers, mushrooms, onions and radishes are reasonable sources. It is now thought that selenium acts in the body by protecting the heart tissue from the damaging effects of free radicals. However, the effects of selenium on extending life and delaying ageing have not been proven and unless the soil or diet is deficient in selenium, it is hard to advocate it in tablet form.

Another natural anti-oxidant which is taken by some longevity-minded individuals is superoxide dismutase or SOD. As mentioned in Chapter Two, this is the anti-oxidant enzyme that specifically roams the body neutralising the highly reactive superoxide free radical. It is part of the body's first line of defence against radicals and is found in all the cells. It also seems to be found on all the shelves of health food stores. However, SOD is such a large molecule that it is almost certainly broken down by enzymes in the stomach and digestive system before it can have an effect on the body.

This rather unsuccessful search for the one and only elixir of youth has in some ways been encouraged by those ageing theorists who have insisted on concentrating their efforts into finding a single cause to explain the ageing process. In the same way, scientists searched for decades for a magic bullet to cure cancer, until it was realised that there was no single disease called cancer, but many different changes in the cells of the body that caused many different types of tumour.

Knowledge about the ageing process is at a much earlier stage than that for cancer, but it is just as likely that there are many mechanisms to account for the changes we describe as ageing, and so many different approaches will be required to slow down or alter the process. Just as with cancer, there is unlikely to be one magic cure for ageing, but techniques which affect just one part of the ageing process could still have a significant impact. So far there are only two completely undisputed anti-ageing regimes that can achieve that; both exert their effects via the body's immune system.

CHAPTER FOUR

Weakened Defences

At first sight, starving for immortality might seem as paradoxical as fighting for peace, but since 1981 an American gerontologist called Roy Walford has been deliberately cutting down his food intake, in the belief that this will prolong his life and allow him to reach his maximum lifespan. As one of America's most respected, albeit eccentric, researchers into ageing, Walford has temporarily parted company with his orthodox colleagues, and like Brown-Séquard before him, is conducting a clinical trial with himself as the subject. However, unlike the members of the Gland Grafters club, Walford's anti-ageing regime is based on credible, scientific data that has withstood the scrutiny of scientific publication. The theory he is putting to the test argues that eating less will prevent the ravages of old age and ultimately increase longevity. So strong is Walford's personal belief in this theory that he is prepared to put his lifespan where his mouth is, and practise what he preaches.

The idea that those who eat less could live longer may sound odd, but it is certainly not new. It is based around a series of classic feeding experiments carried out by a Scotsman in the early 1930s. Clive McCay discovered he could increase the maximum lifespan of rats by reducing their calorie intake by 40 per cent of normal rat fodder, supplemented with extra vitamins and minerals. As well as increasing their lifespan the restricted diet retarded the animals' growth, but otherwise the rats were in good health and presumably good spirits because they were sexually active well into old age and carried on reproducing long after they should have reached the rat menopause.

A variation on this same dietary theme was carried out, again on rats, 10 years later, when scientists studied the effect of intermittent fasting on lifespan. The rats were fed the rodent equivalent of *haute cuisine* on day one and then given nothing but fresh air and water on the second day. The same experiment was carried out on two other groups of animals with fasting taking place on the third, and fourth days. Rats who were allowed to enjoy the good life and gorge themselves to their hearts' content on good cooking lived to see 800 days, but in the three groups who had only been given a little of what they fancied, maximum lifespan shot up to between 1,000 and 1,100 days. This was the equivalent of a 20 to 30 per cent increase in maximum lifespan.

Scientific fascination with the effects of dietary restriction on lifespan continued well into the 1960s and 70s with a long series of experiments carried out by Morris Ross at the Cancer Research Institute in Philadelphia. He experimented on rats which normally lived for between 1,000 and 1,099 days but when fed a calorie-restricted diet could increase this to between 1,600 and 1,699 days. This was an even more impressive result and amounted to a 60 per cent increase in longevity.

The conclusion of all these animal experiments is that eating less can add the human equivalent of between 40 and 80 years to a mammal's life. Almost as important as its life-extending properties is the finding that restricting calories can delay the onset of age-related diseases like heart disease, cancer, arthritis, and kidney disease. Instead of succumbing to one of these typical ageing disorders, most of the underfed rats just died of old age. If the results obtained with rats could ever be translated into human terms, then the implications for ageing are tremendous; eating less could lead to a longer, and more importantly, healthier life.

Walford is prepared to extrapolate from mice, or rats, to men, and has designed his '120-Year Diet' along the lines of the successful rodent recipe. He is at pains to point out that while all the rat experiments restricted calorie intake, the rats' diets were supplemented with essential vitamins and minerals, a dietary regime he has dubbed 'underfeeding without malnutrition'. This means that their diet contained all the nutrients needed to prevent disease, but with about 30 per cent fewer calories than the number required to maintain normal body weight. He is also quick to add that the sort of severe dietary restriction given to rats from the time of weaning could not be applied to humans, and would anyway be undesirable because cutting down calories that early in life would stunt our growth, just as it did in the rats. Nevertheless he is equally convinced that underfeeding can still be used to extend maximum lifespan even when started in middle age. Experiments carried out at the University of Texas support his ideas because when six-month-old rats had their food intake reduced, the effect on maximum lifespan was as impressive as if it had been started at birth. By applying the intermittent fasting regime to rats from the equivalent of middle age (11 to 18 months), scientists at the USA's National Institute on Ageing were able to stretch out their lives by 20 to 40 per cent, well into golden old age. According to Walford, starting his diet half way through life should produce half the life extension one could achieve using the diet from birth, but without the unpleasant side effect of ending up a very long-lived person of small stature.

As far as human beings are concerned, the results of food restriction will depend entirely on the age at which the programme is started. Working on the basis of information from laboratory experiments in which calorie restriction in adult animals worked best when it was imposed very gradually, Walford recommends that dieting should start slowly so that body weight is lost over a long period of time. Ironically, earlier attempts to extend lifespan by severely reducing the diet in adult rats only succeeded in hastening their meeting with the grim rodent reaper. It seems that rats, like us, are not served by crash diets and long periods of self-imposed starvation.

As well as promoting the slow, steady approach to longevity, another golden rule for would-be immortals about to embark on the 120-Year Diet, is that the amount of weight to be lost, however slowly, depends on something called the 'set point'. This apparently is the term used to describe the natural weight of an individual, or indeed any mouse or rat, when eating normally and not fasting or gorging. In order to guarantee a disease-free, long life, Walford's regime calls for a loss of weight of about 10 to 25 per cent below an individual's set point, carried out over a period of between four to six years;

the complete antithesis to the 'crash-dieting' programmes that promise massive weight loss in a matter of weeks.

The exact amount of weight lost on the anti-ageing diet will depend on the original 'set point'. This in turn has been fixed in all of us by a combination of genetics and early feeding experiences. According to Walford, once fixed, the body is very clever at preserving this level by altering the way it extracts energy from food, a process described as metabolic efficiency. If calories are restricted then the body's metabolism shifts up a gear to operate as efficiently on less fuel; if we go on a food binge then the metabolic rate turns down its level of efficiency to tick over at a lower rate. In this way the body attempts to produce a balance of energy payments to keep us hovering around our set point. From Walford's point of view exploiting this balancing act is central to his recipe for longevity; an optimum body weight 10 to 25 per cent below the set point will push metabolic efficiency to its upper limits. To add credibility to his metabolic theory he takes scientific comfort from the farmers in far-off Java, whose metabolic efficiency was found to be 80 per cent *higher* in those with the *lowest* intake of calories (1,535) when compared to farmers with a much higher consumption of food (2,382 calories). It seems that the farmers on the lower diet had adapted to less food and pushed up the body's thermostat, making them metabolically more efficient.

To work out the number of calories needed to achieve slow weight loss over a number of years, Walford went back to scientific literature and came up with a study carried out just after World War Two on young conscientious objectors. When given a strict diet of only 1,600 calories, they lost weight rapidly. After about six months on this diet their bodies had adapted so well and their weight had stabilised so that they could only put on weight if their calorie intake was increased to 2,000 calories a day. Basing his diet around this sort of research, Walford recommends a 2,000 calorie diet for an average-sized man, and 1,800 for a woman, both chosen from the food and menu combinations offered as part of the 120-Year Diet. An alternative route to longer life, personally preferred by Walford, is fasting for one or two days, with more generous helpings of high-calorie food on the eating days.

Transferring the 'undernutrition without malnutrition' experiment from rats to men has not so far fired the imagination of the American people, who do not appear to be queuing eagerly to follow Walford's Pied Piper lead. Undaunted, he claims, quite accurately, that undernutrition is the only method that has been scientifically proven to increase the maximum lifespan of warm-blooded animals, and that it has produced consistent results in every species tested. For him the path to rejuvenation is a straight dietary one, and he reduces his calorie intake by intermittent starvation. For two days of the week Walford eats nothing; for the rest of the week he lives on just over 2,000 calories-worth of carefully chosen food. If he loses more than half to one pound a month in weight, he increases his intake to slow down the dieting process. Honey, sugar, alcohol, refined carbohydrates and extra salt are not on the list of ingredients for the 120-Year Diet. Interestingly, Walford used to lace his frugal diet with liberal helpings of vitamins, minerals and all sorts of exotic anti-oxidants way in excess of recommended doses in the USA. Now, however, he appears to have seen the light, and it no longer shines on the free radical theory of ageing. A former believer in this theory, Walford has now apparently lost his faith, and keeps his chemical supplementation to within more respectable limits, which for many Californians is a great pity, because the pill-popping side of Walford's anti-ageing therapy was in many ways easier to follow than the strict low-calorie diet itself. Walford does, however, issue a serious warning that no one should embark on his dietary regime without first consulting a doctor; it seems unlikely, bearing in mind the conservative nature of British medicine, that many general practitioners in this country would be prepared to condone such an enterprise although in the USA things might be different.

Even though evidence that cutting calories extends maximum lifespan may be conclusive in rats, no comparative research has been carried out on people. So far, the only results of the effect of calorie restriction on humans have come from studies of malnourished people. Scientifically this work is not ideal because it has been impossible to rule out the effects on lifespan of other factors like infection and poor medical care. Walford also emphasises that malnourished subjects will, by definition, have a diet deficient in minerals and vitamins and so his experimental criterion of 'undernutrition without malnutrition' could not be fulfilled and so could not be tested. Ironically, Walford cites observations of patients with Anorexia Nervosa, the slimmers' disease, as support for the beneficial effects of undereating. He rests his bizarre case on the fact that food intake of the anorexic represents an extreme version of the 120-Year Diet, in that sufferers tend to limit their intake of fat and carbohydrates but include vegetables and low-fat cheeses. The sort of weight loss experienced by anorexics is rapid and extreme, although Walford argues that it is still 'undernutrition without malnutrition', and claims that anorexics remain well until about 30 to 40 per cent of their body weight has been lost. Also, compared to the truly mal-nourished, anorexics do not have an increased vulnerability to infections and their immune system remains intact until weight loss becomes excessive.

In direct contrast to these observations are the results of an enormous study of the relationship between lifespan and body weight involving 750,000 men and women, published by the American Cancer Society. According to these results, people who were more than 10 per cent lighter than average tended to have shorter lifespans. At first this seems to directly contradict the various animal experiments that have been carried out so far. Walford counters these scientific critics by suggesting that being 'naturally thin' is not the same as being thin through dietary restriction. He emphasises that people who stay under-weight in spite of excessive food intake tend to have a slightly increased metabolic rate which in turn somehow reduces their lifespan. Walford goes on to argue that people who are under-weight because they eat very sparingly, but don't carefully select what they eat, tend to be malnourished. This is backed up by close examination of some of the animal experiments. When rats were kept on a normal diet and some of them given either protein-rich diets or low-protein diets the researchers discovered that not only did the fat rats die sooner, so did the lean rats. According to Walford this shows the results of poor nutrition, not genuine dietary restriction.

However, if Walford is right, and underfeeding does work, there could be many beneficial side effects to this particular kind of life extension; one is that the onset of age-related disease is significantly delayed in dietary-restricted animals; another is that they appear fitter than normally fed rats. Cancers, cataracts, discolouration and matting of hair, dryness of skin, kidney disease and heart disease are all less frequent in restricted animals than in normal ones. Furthermore the smaller numbers of the restricted animals which do finally develop these diseases do so at a substantially later age than their unrestricted partners. Overall there is less disease, and what there is is postponed. Studies of enzyme activities in dietary-restricted animals show that they differ from normal animals of the same age and fully fed rats of a much younger age. It could be that we are not so much studying a slowing down of the ageing process; rather that dietary restriction pushes the animal on to a completely different developmental pathway.

The main drawback with this long-term one-man experiment is that we won't really know for certain if Walford's 120-Year Diet can extend human lifespan for at least another 50 or 60 years, by which time the information might be of some use to the next generation but will be too late for us. At least Dr Walford himself can take comfort from the fact that he will not be short of an interested audience as he puts himself through years of undernutrition, for, like all good rejuvenators before him, his prescription for longer life has elevated him to celebrity status in age-conscious California.

Walford believes that undernutrition works by protecting the body's defence system, the immune system, from the wear and tear of normal ageing. As we get older, the efficiency of the defence system declines rapidly, so our body is less able to defend itself from attack; perversely the immune system also loses its ability to tell the difference between friend and foe and turns on the body itself, leading to characteristic 'auto-immune' diseases associated with old age, like arthritis. Under-feeding somehow keeps the immune system younger longer, so it can carry on with its vital role of protecting us well into old age.

If underfeeding seems to postpone the ageing of the immune system, Roy Walford also discovered that decreasing body temperature appears to inhibit the harmful auto-immune processes that occur in adulthood, at least in poikilothermic (cold-blooded) fish. He was able to prolong the lifespan of these fish by up to 76 per cent by the simple process of transferring them in middle age from water at 20 degrees centigrade to a tank five degrees cooler. This small temperature difference was enough to exert a powerful effect on the immune system of the fish. Walford then tried his life-extending trick on the shortest-lived fish known to man, called the Annual fish. It seems to have evolved a short lifespan to cope with life in small pools which dry up and so disappear in the summer.

Before the Annual fish die they go through a series of age-related changes; their backs develop a hump and their bodies shorten in length. Inside the body there are microscopic changes in the thyroid gland and liver. Walford discovered that as well as extending the lifespan of the fish, he was able to delay the onset of these changes just by reducing the temperature of the water by a few degrees.

Unlike underfeeding, lowering the temperature of the water had its greatest effect on maximum lifespan if it was carried out during the second half of life. Another curious experimental result was that the two treatments combined had an even greater impact on the lifespan of the fish; by reducing their diet during the early years of life and lowering the water temperature during later years, the maximum lifespan of the fish could be increased by up to 300 per cent. This is very good news if you happen to be a fish with a close relationship with a caring scientist, but for mammals, and in particular, humans, the beneficial effects are less clear cut. Most of the information about the long-term effects of reduced internal body temperature in warm-blooded animals comes from studies of animals that hibernate.

Hibernation is a peculiar physiological state that seems to hover between consciousness and unconsciousness. Socrates is even reputed to have sent out students on early wildlife field trips to observe this mysterious process. The magical ability of hibernating animals to awaken from their state of suspended animation has throughout history stimulated the imagination of creators of fairy tales like Rip Van Winkle and the Sleeping Beauty.

For some time scientists as well as nature lovers had noticed animals that seemed to completely disappear in the cold winter months, to reappear with the first hint of spring, but it has only been in the last 30 years that those scientists have begun to understand why, and to piece together the peculiar biological changes taking place in the animal's body.

Animals who are used to hibernating in the winter prepare themselves by cutting down their normal metabolic activity so they become sleepy. Some of them will need to collect and store food for the winter months; others are able to increase their levels of body fat and rely on this fatty store for winter fuel. By the time the autumn months come to a close the animals stop eating and find a place to sleep. As well as hormone production being reduced, hibernation is now known to involve a reduction in body temperature and breathing. Although it was at first difficult to believe, scientists discovered that animals who are hibernating can stop breathing for periods of time that would normally be considered life threatening.

In spite of promoting a state of near-sleep, hibernation does not make the animal vulnerable to attack by predators because the brain is kept in a normal state of alertness, ready to wake the hibernator at any sign of encroaching danger. This level of brain activity might also explain why hibernators wake up periodically throughout their big sleep irrespective of danger. As the spring gets nearer, perhaps in response to some internal clock, these phases of wakefulness increase in number, and the animal's hormone system is switched on again. Once March approaches, the hibernators are ready for an early morning call.

All these changes are thought to be brought about by the release of a chemical which increases the production in the brain of a natural pain killer or opiate. This literally sedates the animal in preparation for a time of reduced activity. This chemical is also thought to be responsible for keeping the body ticking over at a reduced temperature, which can often be as low as two or three degrees centigrade. This vast reduction in temperature may not, as in the case of the Annual fish, increase the maximum lifespan of the hibernators, but it does seem to have an effect on other processes normally associated with ageing like cross-linking of collagen fibres which is inhibited in the hibernating animal as is the loss of calcium from the bones. This last result is surprising, since hibernating animals do not use their limbs for weeks or months at a time.

However, as intriguing as this work is, it is hard to see how humans could benefit from hibernation as a way to ward off the diseases of old age and live a longer, healthier life. Even if the hibernating chemical that initiates the whole process could be found and synthesised, there would be little point in living longer if it entailed spending one's extended life asleep, waiting to be woken by a kiss from a very aged prince.

The life-extending potential of hibernation is not only unappealing, it might anyway prove physiologically impossible. For mammals that do not hibernate it is remarkably difficult to lower body temperature because we have developed a system that will keep our body temperature as near to 37 degrees centigrade as possible. Even when there are extreme changes in the outside temperature, our internal body temperature remains constant because of a delicate, but very effective control process called homeostasis. This whole system is controlled centrally by a trigger located in a portion of the brain called the hypothalamus. Once the brain receives information about the temperature of the blood, the hypothalamus sends messages to the rest of the body to turn the body's central heating system up or down. If body temperature falls below the reference point set by the hypothalamus, we start shivering. This increases metabolism and body temperature rises. If we get too hot, sweating is stimulated so that heat is lost and body temperature falls. Extra information about body temperature is supplied by nerve sensors in the extremities of the body, so that if we go out on a cold day, the message to shiver can be sent from the brain without having to wait for the body temperature to fall. This integrated system of temperature sensors ensures that our internal temperature does not fluctuate too much around the 37 degree mark.

Of course, if we had easy access to the thermostat in the hypothalamus, we would be in a position to reset it and lower our body temperature. This is the way that hibernation manages to achieve its effect, by carefully lowering the thermostat to a level almost equal to the external temperature, so that vital energy will not be wasted in keeping the body warm during the long winter months. Since this process of resetting the hypothalamus during hibernation is carried out by a number of warm-blooded animals who can successfully reduce their body temperatures to almost freezing point, and who are very similar to us physiologically, some scientists have suggested that the sort of damage we suffer when our body temperature falls below 37 degrees may just be the observed side effect of the hypothalamus trying to reset the thermostat. This could possibly mean that the effects on the body of extremely low temperatures might not be as harmful as once thought. According to this idea, the observed death of cells and tissues at freezing temperatures might be misleading and the body could still be functioning, but at a much reduced rate. However, this new approach to temperature regulation does not appear to have immediate applications for ageing research.

For the moment any thought of being able artificially to lower our body temperature as a means to longer life must remain in the realms of science fiction, although in India it has been claimed that some Yogis can reset their central thermostat by as much as one degree fahrenheit using a combination of meditation and breathing exercises. This ability to lower body temperature has been linked to claims that Yogis live extremely long lives. However there is no concrete scientific proof nor are there any reliable birth certificates to uphold these assertions.

It does seem that interfering with the immune system as a way to prolong life does not offer an easy route to the fountain of youth; intermittent fasting and meditation are likely to attract only the most dedicated follower of longevity.

If keeping cool isn't the best way to a longer life, there is some evidence that raising body temperature can have the opposite effect and shorten lifespan. Increased body temperature again achieves this effect via the immune system. For some reason the cells that make up the immune system work best at a temperature higher than the normal 37 degrees. One of the reasons we know this is because of work carried out with cancer patients; when their body temperature was deliberately raised five degrees above normal, the cells in their immune system were much more efficient at combating their tumours. These sorts of studies have led scientists to propose that the body deliberately raises its temperature to boost the efficiency of the immune system and fight off the infection. This is a process we refer to as fever.

A fever is produced when a specific protein is released from immune cells under attack by the invading organism. This protein travels via various chemical intermediates back to the hypothalamus where it resets the body's thermostat and raises body temperature. At this higher temperature the cells in the immune system can fight the infection faster. The bouts of sweating and shivering that normally accompany a fever were thought at one time to be harmful, but recent research now suggests they are just the side effects of this important protective mechanism.

The ability to raise body temperature to produce a fever is common throughout the animal kingdom, but at first sight this process of fighting infection is difficult to comprehend in terms of evolution; it would seem much more sensible for body temperature to be set at a point at which the immune system can function more efficiently – in other words higher than 37 degrees centigrade. One theory suggests that our body temperature is set lower than this to prevent the immune system from damaging the body. Although it might sound odd that the very system designed to protect us from attack could possibly turn on the body, as we get older that is precisely what does happen; the immune system fails to tell the difference between what is us and what is foreign and launches an unprovoked attack on the body itself. For some reason, the higher temperatures produced during a fever are thought to increase the risk of an auto-immune response and speed up the ageing process. Evolution seems to have favoured a body temperature at which the risk of auto-immune disease was low, but there was still the option to boost the temperature and so the efficiency of the immune system.

Roy Walford believes that the gradual decline in the immune system as we get older plays a major role in the ageing process. In the elderly, the body's defences are weakened in two ways; not only does the immune system turn on the body's own cells, it also fails to identify and kill invading organisms; hence with age we grow more susceptible to diseases like cancer and suffer repeated infections. The reason for this decline in the immune system is not understood and although reduced temperature and underfeeding may slow it down, an impaired immune system is part and parcel of growing old.

It has been suggested that the breakdown in the immune system starts when it loses the ability to recognise slight changes in molecular structure so that cells which have mutated and would normally be destroyed by the immune system are ignored and allowed to grow. Even if mutant cells are recognised, the ageing immune system may not be able to produce enough antibodies to fight off the foreign invaders that cause acute infection. Eventually antibodies are produced which attack the normal cells inside the body causing the auto-immune diseases of ageing.

Walford thinks all these effects could be explained by the action of a group of genes located quite close together on a single chromosome – chromosome number six. The collection is called the major histocompatability complex (MHC). The MHC is already known to carry the genetic information that allows the immune system to distinguish between friend and foe, so that organ grafts survive best if donor and recipient are of the same MHC type. This theory suggests that any damage suffered by the genes of the MHC would have serious consequences for the normal functioning of the immune system. More importantly for ageing research, the MHC is also closely linked to longevity – at least in mice.

In 1977 Roy Walford and his colleagues at UCLA Medical School studied different strains of mice which were genetically identical except for differences in their histocompatability complex. They found that the lifespan of the mice was directly related to these differences; the MHC appeared to regulate maximum lifespan in some way. Walford believes that the MHC controls lifespan via a small cluster of genes colourfully described as the 'supergene'. This supergene apparently has a direct effect on maximum lifespan via systems in the body like the immune system, the brain and the hormone-secreting glands. But, however clear cut these results are in mice, the relationship between the MCH and maximum lifespan in humans has never been proved.

The only way to test this 'supergene' theory would be to transfer the supergene from a longer-living species into a shorter-lived species and see if there was any increase in lifespan. These experiments have yet to be performed. As for experimenting with this technique in humans, fortunately or unfortunately, the human is already one of the longest-lived animals, and there is no way to get a suitable gene complex to transplant from a longer-lived animal.

Supergene or no supergene, Walford has proposed a theory to explain how changes in the MHC could influence the immune system and so contribute to ageing. In a healthy person the immune system functions efficiently until puberty. One way to explain this decline at the level of the cell is to think in terms of damage to the genetic information contained in the DNA. As we discovered in Chapter Two, proponents of the Error Theory believe that as we get older we accumulate damage in our DNA and once this damage outstrips the body's repair system, 'errors' build up so that eventually the DNA sends out faulty instructions and abnormal cells are produced. According to Walford, the histocompatability complex may fail to recognise the altered cells and order an immune system attack on them, causing them further damage. At the same time, the histocompatability complex itself accumulates damage so that its identity code becomes less precise. As a result it loses the ability to recognise foreign invaders, and cannot instruct the immune system to destroy them. Eventually the histocompatability complex code is so damaged that the instructions sent to the immune system become garbled and it starts to produce auto-antibodies that will attack normal cells. This continuing cycle of damage illustrates the underlying idea on which the 'Error Theory' is based, since these 'errors' will – eventually – lead to total breakdown, or catastrophe. The number of auto-antibodies increases rapidly with age, and they bring with them the continual threat of cancer.

Meanwhile the immune system itself accumulates damage. It becomes less able to carry out the 'search and destroy' instructions of the MHC, and foreign cells and substances start to accumulate. As the strength of the immune system declines, so vulnerability to degenerative disease increases. Walford estimates that by 70 years of age the immune system may have lost 90 per cent of its fighting capacity. This theory is very attractive because it integrates cell theories of ageing with age changes throughout the whole body, but as yet is not conclusively proven.

That decrease in immunity just after puberty is thought to be reflected in the shrinking of the thymus gland, a mass of tissue that lies just over the heart. This gland begins to shrink with the onset of puberty and has shrivelled to a mere three grams by the age of 60. Because of this decline many scientists thought its role in the body was unimportant. It is now known that the thymus controls an army of cells that recognise and destroy dangerous invaders. To do this, a family of hormones called the thymosins are produced which instruct the cell army. This understanding of the organisation of the immune system and the role of the thymus as its master gland did not begin to emerge until the early 1960s.

It was not until 1961 that researchers at the University of Minnesota discovered that mice failed to grow and eventually died if their thymus glands were removed at birth. This research was to lead to the idea that the thymus gland is crucial not only to the day-to-day functioning of the immune system, but also the growth of the whole organism.

Three years later, Alan Goldstein, a young post-doctoral student at the Albert Einstein College of Medicine in New York, was asked to conduct an almost impossible search for a hormone secreted by the thymus gland. He was to successfully extract and identify the thymus hormones which were named thymosins. Through the course of this work Goldstein was to discover that the thymus and its hormones control the production of white blood cells known as T cells. (They are called T cells because they are controlled by the thymus gland.) The thymosins exert their effects on three very different types of T cells: killer cells, which as their name suggests kill foreign invaders; helper cells which 'help' in the production of antibodies; and suppressor cells which prevent or suppress the immune system from attacking the body's own tissue and causing auto-immune diseases. Once activated by the thymosins, these T cells circulate through the body, mainly ending up in the spleen and the lymph nodes. Just like the MHC, if the cells of the thymus gland are damaged by genetic factors or by environmental agents like radiation or toxins, the immune system suffers. This could lead to cancer, life-threatening infections and auto-immune diseases like rheumatoid arthritis.

It is now also understood that there are two different components of the immune system in the body. One half of the system is made up of the thymus and its T cells which destroy invaders; the second half of the system is made up of white cells called B cells which are responsible for the production of antibodies. The two systems work together under the control of the thymus gland so that the thymosin hormones transform white cells into T cells and in doing so keep a tight control over the balance of killer T cells to suppressor T cells. In turn, suppressor T cells can restrain the B cells from attacking the body's own tissues.

From the results of his experiments, Goldstein decided that any abnormality in the numbers of the three types of T cells could lead to poor health. In the early seventies he had a rare opportunity to test out his theories on a young Californian girl called Heather, who was born with a condition called thymic hypoplasia which means her body did not make enough T cells. At five years of age, Heather's immune system resembled that of an elderly person. Much of Heather's early life was spent inside a San Francisco hospital. With no functioning thymus gland to control T cell production, Heather had no immune protection and was open to every possible infection; her life was under threat. At the age of nine months her parents had been told she would be lucky to see her fifth birthday. Just when time was running out she was examined by Alan Goldstein.

Goldstein was already aware that when a solution of thymosin hormone was given to mice in which the thymus gland had been completely removed, their immune systems were restored. The addition of the thymosin hormone had transformed the cells that made up the marrow inside the bones into T cells. Goldstein decided to use this technique to try to restart Heather's immune system, but he had to work fast.

Goldstein's laboratory worked around the clock to purify enough thymosin from calf glands to give her the immune protection she desperately needed. The treatment was an unqualified success.

Heather was very lucky. Until a few years ago children born without a functioning thymus gland usually died in early childhood from overwhelming infections or were destined to spend their lives in plastic germ-free bubble enclosures. Today she is a normal 18-year-old. For the past five years she has not needed to take thymosin because her own T cells seem to have taken over. Heather was the very first person to receive thymosin, and her dramatic clinical improvement accelerated interest in the potential of using thymic hormones to raise immunity as we age.

Like Heather's, the thymus glands of the elderly produce inadequate amounts of T cells. Instead of suffering from the sort of acute illnesses and infections that were life-threatening to Heather, an ageing thymus leaves our immune systems in a state of reduced activity. However, the pattern of immune deficiency is the same in both and the solution to the problem may also be the same. If, as for Heather, artificial supplies of thymosin could be given throughout old age, it should be possible to boost the number of T cells and improve immunity. Rejuvenating the immune system with thymosin could add perhaps a dozen years to our average lifespan by fighting off cancer, arthritis, pneumonia and many other diseases which appear with old age.

Although it is unlikely that thymosin will ever be given prophylactically to prevent ageing, some ageing cancer patients already receive injections of thymosin as part of their treatment. It is hoped these injections will boost their already weakened immune systems and also protect them from further damage by radiation and chemotherapy treatments used to combat their cancers. The early results are said to be encouraging. At the University of California Medical Center in San Francisco doctors have reported that thymosin is having a positive effect in patients with advanced adenocarcinoma, a cancer of the adrenal gland which is normally very difficult to treat and has a poor prognosis.

Alan Goldstein now makes thymosin using modern genetic

engineering techniques. This new form of synthetic thymosin has been used to treat patients with lung cancer. Only 22 per cent of men and 28 per cent of women who contract the commonest form of lung cancer survive more than two years. The new treatment has produced the first improvement on these figures for 50 years, with 33 per cent of patients of both sexes surviving over two years even though their cancers had advanced to a stage which made them inoperable. If the results can now be confirmed in other studies, this work will represent a major breakthrough in cancer treatment.

There is hope too that thymosin can be put to effective use against other disorders, such as auto-immune diseases like rheumatoid arthritis, systemic lupus erythematosis, and multiple sclerosis, all of which are distinguished by an abnormally over-responsive immune system that attacks the body's own normal tissues. Thymosin injections could possibly be used to increase the number of suppressor T cells and so slow down the production of auto-antibodies.

Alan Goldstein's most recent work suggests that the thymus has an even more important role in the body than he originally thought; as well as regulating the immune system, the thymosins appear to have an effect on the brain. Goldstein discovered that the release of hormones from the thymus could trigger the brain to release one of its own hormones called adrenocorticotrophic hormone (ACTH) which in turn acts on the adrenal gland to pump out stress hormones. Even more interesting was the discovery that these stress hormones travelled full circle back to the thymus gland where they inhibited the release of more thymosins and so regulated their own release.

This sort of finding was remarkable because for many years the immune system was thought to operate as an independent unit, but other breakthroughs in immune research have confirmed Goldstein's idea that the immune system is very closely linked to the brain, particularly the psyche, and the claim that the normal efficiency of the immune system can be reduced by changes in emotion, mood and stress. This whole area of research has spawned a controversial new discipline that goes by the name of psychoneuroimmunology or PNI. Proponents of PNI argue that the pathway between the immune system and the brain is two way, with various hormones acting as its messengers. So as well as the immune system acting on the brain, the brain can also influence the immune system. This forms the main area of scientific controversy, since it is extremely difficult to determine the exact effect of something as indefinable as the psyche on the workings of any part of the body.

We are all aware that the mind can, in certain circumstances, influence the body; it is a process exploited to full advantage by the pornography industry where mental images are used to produce physical arousal. Certainly the idea that the mind can promote or conquer disease is no longer new or unorthodox, and explains the homage paid to the placebo effect, but there is still a considerable degree of controversy in the scientific community over the exact way in which the mind can exert its effects.

One of the most surprising ways in which the brain can interact with the immune system was discovered by chance in 1975. Just as Pavlov's dogs had been conditioned to salivate on hearing a bell, Robert Ader at the Rochester School of Medicine in the US conditioned mice to avoid saccharin. This was achieved by feeding the saccharin and at the same time injecting a drug that would inhibit the immune system and cause stomach problems. By linking the two events together in their minds, the mice were taught to avoid saccharin. When the mice were next given saccharin, without the unpleasant drug, those that had received the highest doses in the initial experiment died. Ader was astonished and could only speculate that somehow the conditioning response was so strong that saccharin on its own could kill the animals.

Working out a mechanism to explain this effect is not easy. Immediately after an animal is subjected to psychological stress or is put into a situation that generates anxiety, the brain sends signals which set in motion a chain reaction of biological effects. First of all nerve impulses in the brain transmit messages to the hypothalamus to trigger the release of ACTH from the pituitary gland. This hormone travels to the kidneys where it stimulates the adrenal glands to release stress hormones like cortisol and adrenaline which have powerful effects on the rest of the body. Adrenaline increases the heart rate and blood pressure in preparation for a fast getaway. The stomach releases a hormone called gastrin which speeds up the digestive processes. Cortisol seems to act on the immune system, reducing the number of circulating T cells and shrinking the thymus gland. Over short periods of stress the animal seems able to cope with these changes. However very high levels of cortisol are thought to lead to permanent damage, particularly to the spleen and the thymus. Under extreme conditions the brain may also release its own natural pain killers called endorphins; at high concentrations these can damage the immune system by lowering the efficiency of some kinds of T cells. Changes as severe as these will reduce the effectiveness of the immune system and leave the animal prone to infection and disease.

Since 1981, scientists in Ohio have been studying the different ways in which the brain influences the body's immunity to disease. In one study medical students labouring under the stress of impending examinations were found to have much lower levels of natural killer cells, which, as mentioned earlier, kill any invading organisms. Those students who were lonely as well as stressed had even lower levels of killer white cells.

This is not a new idea. Researchers have known for years that the loss of support from friends and relatives increases a person's risk of disease. The importance of social ties was underlined in an American study of nearly 5,000 men and women in California. Researchers discovered that the increase in mortality was more than double among men and nearly triple among the women who had the fewest friends and social contacts. There was also a significant increase in the death rate among those who felt the least satisfaction with their lives. The results are surprisingly consistent; recently bereaved men were more likely to die than married men of the same age; a study of recently widowed men carried out in New York found that their production of killer white cells was still depressed up to 14 months after their wives had died.

The Californian team went on to study a group of women who had been recently separated or divorced. They wanted to find out if the increased mortality seen in these people was due to a direct effect on the immune system, or just self-neglect due to depression. The results showed that the women's immune systems were depressed and this depression was brought about by the lowered activity of their killer cells.

If divorce is detrimental to the health of our immune systems, then so is staying with the wrong partner. In a group of 38 married women, those whose marriages were poor were psychologically depressed. Their white cells were reduced and responded badly in tests designed to measure their immune response. In terms of the immune system, divorce and bereavement do reduce immunity but only over a short period of time; living with a partner you don't get on with could mean subjecting yourself to a lifetime of reduced immunity and so reducing your life expectancy.

It doesn't always have to be the levels of stress that cause the damage but the way that our bodies respond to that stressful situation. A British study monitored the health of nearly 3,000 women. It was discovered that those who were least able to cope with stress were more likely to get breast cancer. Each woman was given a questionnaire describing potentially stressful life events, and asked to write down which of them had happened to them in the previous two years. Then they were asked to number the life events from one to ten in order of the degree of stress they had experienced with each one. The most interesting result was that the women who had developed cancer appeared to have experienced *fewer* stressful life events than those who were in normal health. When these results were analysed in more detail it was discovered that the patients who developed cancer had perceived their life events as being much more stressful, even though there were fewer of them.

Theories connecting personality and emotions to malignancy date at least from the second century BC when Greek physicians attributed cancer to a melancholy disposition, but although the British researchers found a significant link between breast cancer and stress, it is impossible to state categorically that stress causes breast cancer. What the scientists do agree on is that some women who have early, undiagnosed cancer may increase their chances of that cancer taking hold by their inability to cope with a stressful situation. This will inhibit their immune system at a time when their killer cells should be fighting the cancer.

Studies in which large samples of people are psychologically tested early in life and followed for decades to chart the appearance of various types of cancer are rare. One such project, in which researchers followed nearly 7,000 residents of Almeda County in California for 17 years, showed that two types of isolation – having few close friends and feeling alone even when friends are present – played an important role in increasing the risk of dying from cancer, but only among women. The greatest number of deaths were from breast and lymph cancer.

Scientists have now identified four main factors that seem to be linked to stress; factor one includes all the traumatic life events like bereavement, financial problems, divorce and life-threatening illness; factor two is described as our inherited physiological susceptibility to the damaging effects of stressful events; factor three concerns itself with our psychological ability to handle stress while factor four encompasses the level of stress that is actually beneficial.

This last description may sound contradictory, but as we will discover in Chapter Five, a certain amount of stress is needed to keep us happy and motivated. Old age is often characterised by a feeling of lack of motivation. When a group of nursing-home patients were given control over everyday decisions such as the furnishings in their rooms, they developed improved memory and alertness and had lower levels of stress-related hormones. For them the minor stress of making decisions regarding their own lives had been beneficial. However, some younger people appear to drive themselves too hard and in the process increase their levels of stress, and their susceptibility to disease.

This idea came into vogue nearly 30 years ago when American doctors described a 'coronary-prone behaviour pattern', now usually referred to as Type A. This Type A behaviour was characterised by an aggressive competitiveness together with an intense, sustained drive for achievement, and a pressing sense of time.

This personality classification was to attract world-wide scientific interest because men with Type A behaviour had double the risk of suffering a first heart attack and an even greater risk of a second. The research was done initially with men but the same results seemed to apply to women. In 1978 the National Heart, Lung and Blood Institute in the USA officially condoned this research when it decided that the link between Type A behaviour and coronary heart disease was of the same order of magnitude as the risk associated with age, elevated blood pressure and blood cholesterol, and smoking.

However, the whole concept is now thought to be too limited in its social and cultural perspective. For example, in a long-term study on government civil servants in London's Whitehall, Type A behaviour was more common in higher grades of employment, while death from heart attacks was more common in the lower grades. Type A behaviour as conventionally defined cannot explain these differences in mortality. Following on from these sort of experiments, the term 'stress' was broadened to include all 'psychological' factors such as unemployment and social interaction.

Of the four 'stress' factors, one of the easiest to change is number three, by increasing a person's ability to cope with stress. An effective way to do this is to teach them to relax. In addition to the obvious psychological benefits of relieving stress and mental tension, the findings suggest that, if practised regularly, deep relaxation can strengthen the immune system. These medical advantages cannot be gained from ordinary relaxation activities like gardening or reading, but from intensive techniques like meditation, yoga or biofeedback that induce a specific psychological state.

Relaxation seems to be beneficial because it lowers blood pressure and slows heart and breathing rates. New research suggests that along with these changes come shifts in hormone levels that seem to produce beneficial effects on the immune system. For example, relaxation training by medical students during examinations was found to increase the level of killer cells so they were better able to defend themselves against infectious diseases.

There has also been an enormous interest in using relaxation techniques to reduce the risk of heart disease. A recent report in the *British Medical Journal* noted that patients who had been trained to relax had been able to reduce their blood pressure by a significant amount, and maintained the reduction four years later. Other studies have found these techniques improve the flow of blood to the heart, lower cholesterol levels and lessen the severity of angina attacks.

Research carried out at Harvard Medical School found that regular sessions of a simple meditation technique decreased the body's response to noradrenaline, one of the hormones released in response to stress. Although noradrenaline was still released, the hormone did not seem to have its usual effects.

If relaxation alone can improve our defence system, some scientists go on to claim that visualising certain specific images can enhance the effect. This idea follows the argument that if the psyche can influence the immune system in a negative, damaging way, then perhaps it is possible to harness its powers to positive effect.

Dr Nicholas Hall at George Washington University in the US, is one of the believers; he thinks that it is possible to use mental imagery to boost the immune system. His research team is engaged in several studies, one of which involves cancer patients who supplement their normal treatment with mental therapy. The key to the treatment is for patients to imagine their immune systems playing an active, aggressive role in attacking cancer cells in their bodies. Some people learn how to think of their bodies as a garden with the cancer as a weed that has to be removed; others adopt a military attitude where the cancer becomes the enemy and the white cells are the knights in shining armour, ready to fight and kill any cancer cells. Whatever mental image is chosen by the patient, the overall aim is to think in a positive way to activate the components of their immune systems to eliminate the cancer.

This particular study is still in its infancy, but early results appear encouraging, although whether this is due solely to the positive effects of mental imagery or to the support gained from being part of a group is difficult to work out.

In the UK, this sort of self-hypnosis using mental imagery is being tried out at the Great Ormond Street Hospital in London. Doctors at the hospital are conducting a pilot study in which children are taught techniques of self-hypnosis to relieve the symptoms of diseases that have a psychosomatic element, such as eczema and asthma. The study started from the hypothesis that these sorts of diseases are aggravated by stress and emotional factors. Standard hypnotic techniques were used and about three-quarters of the children in the study were successfully hypnotised. All of them showed improvement in sleeping and self confidence. However, this form of self-hypnosis does not visibly affect the disease, it just makes life with disease more bearable. For the proponents of mental imagery for cancer patients, the aim is to directly affect the disease and halt the growth of the tumour.

This approach has its critics. In a controversial editorial in the *New England Journal of Medicine* senior deputy editor Marcia Angell seriously questioned whether mental attitude affects health and wrote, 'it is time to acknowledge that our belief in disease as a direct reflection of mental state is largely folklore'. She went on to argue that this belief had led to limited and biased research which claimed certain types of personality were prone to disease, and insisted that an emphasis on psychological factors would lead to the misinterpretation of causes and effects of disease. According to Angell, 'we have let our standards slip a bit because we are too ready to accept our mental state as a major and direct cause or cure of disease'. She also feared that linking health to mental discipline might instil an enormous sense of guilt in patients who succumb to illness in spite of a positive approach to life.

Angell believed that the scientific basis for linking attitude to disease was unfounded, and that the known physiological effects of stress on the adrenal glands had been overinterpreted so that stress could be blamed as the cause of a number of diseases.

Some of the opinions stated in Angell's editorial will have been shared by the medical and scientific communities but, despite her cutting attack, most researchers in the field of psychoneuroimmunology still believe in the link between the mind and the body, although they do agree that they are a little thin on scientific proof. The debate over whether emotions and feelings are indeed fundamentally biochemical in nature will continue to rage for many years to come, but in June 1987 the editor of the British journal *The Lancet*, wrote that 'research into the links between the psyche and immunity has three important clinical implications. Psychological treatments might be used as adjunctive therapy to suppress the immune response in life-threatening disease as well as in less serious disorders. Equally, such treatments could be used to enhance the immune system, particularly in vulnerable groups. This research may also shed light on the importance of the protection provided by a positive approach to life.'

In terms of the immune system, adopting a positive approach to life can do no harm, and might do some good, particularly as we get older and our immune system starts to decline. By keeping ourselves stimulated and motivated well into old age we will also reap the benefits, not necessarily in the immune system, but almost certainly in the brain itself.

CHAPTER FIVE

As Old as You Think . . .

Of all the changes that happen to our bodies as we grow old, those that affect the brain are often the most frightening. Most people would willingly tolerate the physical losses and inconveniences of old age in exchange for a mind that can still function properly. As long as our intellect remains intact, we can express ourselves as individuals. Once our mental integrity has been lost, we lose our human identity.

However, it is now accepted that mental decline is not a normal part of the ageing process. Severe loss of memory and intellectual deterioration are not inevitable companions of old age, but symptoms of a number of diseases collectively known as dementia. These diseases are now yielding up some of their secrets under an onslaught of scientific investigation. Since the early 1980s the American Government has increased the budget for research into dementia from less than half a million dollars to well over 15 million.

The American Senate committee recently held the first ever hearing on the dementias of ageing. Some scientists believe that the great leaps forward in research into brain ageing over the last few years have even begun to change the public's attitude to dementia; they go so far as to call it a revolution in thinking about dementia, with people no longer regarding the condition as hopeless.

Of course this was not always the case; up until very recently any elderly patient with symptoms of mental degeneration was diagnosed as senile and dismissed as incurable. It is now understood that at least a quarter of all dementias are reversible, including those caused by brain tumours, depression, or just the hormone imbalances that take place during normal ageing. For those cases of dementia that cannot be cured, about 50 per cent are due to a specific disease called Alzheimer's disease, while the rest can usually be accounted for by the after-effects of minor strokes. The new breed of medical researchers working on the brain are starting to challenge the old belief that ageing is a time of mental decline and suggest that intellectual growth can continue well into old age.

The impact of scientific research on public attitudes towards ageing cannot be overstated. Many ageing experts are convinced that the old pessimistic propaganda about ageing and mental decline may have turned into a self-fulfilling prophecy. On the other hand, those among the ageing who do not accept the stereotypes of helpless old age will remain mentally active well into old age.

One of the major areas of research into brain ageing is on the changes in memory that take place as we age. At the Max Planck Institute in West Berlin, a study has been carried out to measure the extent of the decline of memory in the elderly. The memory experiment was carried out using a mixed group of young and old people and involved learning a set of information using a specific memory trick. First of all the subjects had to memorize a number of landmarks along a walk through West Berlin and then, when presented with a list of objects to be remembered, had to form a mental association between the object and the landmark. The more bizarre the association the more vivid the memory. The objects to be remembered were flashed onto a computer screen as fast as the subject could identify them and link them to the Berlin itinerary. At the end of the experiment the subjects had to be able to type out a list of the objects in the correct order.

If, for example, the first landmark in the journey was a church and the first word presented on the screen was 'flower', then one way to remember the two facts by association would be to think of flowers growing around the church. The researchers were amazed to find that their elderly subjects could memorize 20 words in 50 seconds and reproduce them in the correct order afterwards. When this same test was given to younger subjects there was another surprise. By comparing the performance of the young subjects with their older counterparts, the research team found that accuracy was the same for both groups. The only difference between the groups was the slower speed at which new memories were encoded by the elderly – one 24-year-old was able to memorize each object in half a second.

What this study indicates is that there is still the ability for positive change, for new learning, as we get older, but at a reduced rate. Not surprisingly, ageing is a time of slowing down and our memories reflect that change. The easiest way to describe this system is to think of memory as being made up of two fundamental processes; learning new information and recalling old information at a later date. These two processes are thought to be linked in some way inside the brain.

Brains are similar to computers in so much as they operate using electrical signals. The brain circuits that run on these signals are made up of nerve cells called neurones which transmit electrical impulses along their length. Each neurone is made up of a central part called the cell body which is surrounded by a mass of thin branches called dendrites which send electrical messages from surrounding nerve cells into the cell body. There is also a much bigger branch called an axon, which transports the signal out of the cell body to the next neurone along, and so continues the chain of information. There are about 1,000 billion neurones in the brain each connecting with as many as 10,000 other nerve cells, so the potential number of connections between them can be in the region of trillions. It is not surprising that the electrical circuitry in a single human brain involves more connections than all the telephone networks in the world.

This complexity is possible because our brains also make use of chemicals. Axons and dendrites are never physically in contact with each other. Each axon is separated from the dendrite of the next cell by a small gap called a synapse. In order to get across the gap, the electrical message causes the release of a chemical called a neurotransmitter. When a message reaches the end of the axon, molecules of the chemical transmitter are released into the synapse where they diffuse across the gap and attach themselves to tailor-made holes called receptors on the surface of the adjacent dendrite. This interaction between the chemical transmitter and the receptor is very specific, with the receptor acting as a lock which can only be opened by one particular chemical key. Once the key is in the right lock, the electrical message can be passed down the dendrite to the next cell body, and so on. This description is oversimplified; in reality dendrites can transmit as well as receive messages, while axons can inhibit the output of other axons. In this way the brain can record over 86 billion bits of information every day while our memories are estimated to hold 100 trillion pieces of information in a lifetime.

However, explaining memory in terms of chemical transmitters is not easy. The simplest memory system would be one in which one neurone was used just for one specific memory. So, for example, if one of our neurones represents the memory of the dog, then this cell will transmit an electrical message every time the dog is recognised but will not respond to the sight of the cat or the budgie. This theory sounds seductively simple, but there is a problem since such a simpli-fied system would not leave enough storage space to accommodate the vast number of different memories that we have formed for each subject. If there was one neurone for each memory we had of the dog there wouldn't be much room left for anything else.

It is now known that information to be remembered is filed away in at least two different memory stores; short-term memory which is the memory of very recent events and is very easily disrupted, and long-term memory, which is much more stable and will retain its stored information even after head injury or traumatic events like epileptic fits. For reasons not really understood, not all the information in the short-term memory goes on to be stored in the long-term memory depot. This means that there must be some sort of memory sieve that files important memories and junks the rest; without it we would be lost, with our long-term memory filled with useless observations. It would be very helpful if these complicated tricks of memory could be reduced to the level of neurones and chemical transmitters because then it might be possible to develop drugs which could act on the cells to improve memory, and combat the sort of forgetfulness seen during ageing.

It has already been suggested that the changes in memory associated with old age, particularly changes in short-term memory, might be due to falling levels of one particular chemical transmitter called acetylcholine. This theory was supported when young adults who had been given drugs to block the production of acetylcholine in their brains had difficulties with memory similar to those experienced by older individuals.

If it was true that levels of acetylcholine are increased when a memory is formed and reduced in ageing brains, then it was logical to assume that increasing acetylcholine levels in ageing patients would improve memory. Supplies of acetylcholine are manufactured in the brain from choline, a substance found naturally in the diet, so early attempts to increase levels of the transmitter concentrated on increasing the amounts of choline in the diet. In animals this had the desired effect; middle-aged mice could remember more when they were put on a choline-rich diet. Unfortunately choline therapy for ageing humans with defective memories has so far been unsuccessful in at least 10 human studies.

This discrepancy between the human and animal results may be due to the fact that in animals it is possible to increase choline in the diet at an early age and carry on the therapy for a long period of time. This is generally not the case in human studies where treatment, even if extended over a number of months, makes up only a very limited part of the human lifespan. Also, in most of the patients, choline therapy is started at a time when damage to the brain's acetylcholine system may already be irreversible.

Whatever the chemical basis for memory, it does seem to alter with age. The sort of memory skills that remain intact are those which do not rely on the context in which they were learned in order to be remembered – for example, knowing how to fit the pieces into a jigsaw puzzle, where the act of remembering seems minimal. However, for tasks that demand straight recall, the decline in memory can start as early as the age of 30, will be noticeable by the age of 40 and will continue steadily from that point on. One easy way to combat irritating memory losses as we age is to rely more heavily on memory aids – like writing out lists for the supermarket or jotting down telephone numbers.

*

The changes in learning and memory abilities seen in some of the elderly may be due to structural changes taking place inside the brain itself. As we get older the brain shrinks and this shrinking seems to be due to a loss of neurones in a particular part of the brain called the cortex. With advancing age the dendrites, which form the point of contact with other nerve cells, start to shrink or in some cases disappear altogether. What is surprising is that results from animal experiments suggest it is possible for the remaining healthy neurones to grow new dendrites to compensate for the loss.

It is not known whether humans too can regrow parts of the nerve cells so that when some neurones die or fail to change, others can take over their job, but an unusual clue was provided by the dulcet tones of the canary. Fernando Nottebohm at Rockefeller University in New York has been studying the parts of the brain canaries use when they sing. The amount of singing a canary does depends on what time of the year it is; in springtime a male canary's fancy turns to love and one way to impress the opposite sex is to sing your heart out. Nottebohm discovered that the song centre in a canary's brain, called the *hyperstriatum ventrate pars caudale* or HVC, changes size depending on whether or not it is being used. In the spring, when the canary is developing its mating song, the HVC recruits neurones from surrounding areas, a process triggered by a surge of the male sex hormone, testosterone. In the autumn, when singing loses its former appeal, the canary's HVC discards excess neurones, shrinking back to its original size. He discovered that male impresarios with particularly large song repertoires had bigger HVC's than their less fortunate competitors.

More surprising was Nottebohm's discovery that if testosterone was given to a female canary, she was not only able to sing, but her HVC also increased in size. These changes could be explained by the formation of new connections between the female canary's nerve cells; dendrites in the canary brain expand by about 30 per cent in size during the song-learning period and after four weeks of receiving male sex hormones, females produce 50 per cent more nerve junctions or synapses.

However Dr Nottebohm's team followed up this work with

an experiment which showed that it was not simply a case of the nerve connections increasing, but the fact that new brain cells were being made. They injected canaries with a radioactive component of DNA and managed to track its course to the cells in the HVC. The fresh DNA was being used to form new cells in the canary's brain. One of the researchers was even able to record the electrical signals transmitted between the new, radioactive labelled brain cells. Radioactive DNA also ended up in the HVC of females who had not been given any male sex hormone. This was odd because in these females the HVC did not increase in size, so old cells must have been killed to make room for the new radioactively labelled ones. It is now thought that the females use this new growth to be able to recognize the latest hits in the canary top ten without having to sing them.

It is too early to know whether the same process happens in humans and whether neurones continue to develop after birth, although Nottebohm seems optimistic. If this was the case then the brain might not only be able to learn and adjust throughout life but it may be able to do so by forming new dendrites, new synaptic connections and perhaps even new neurones. However, Dr Nottebohm's work does have its critics, and scientists have found no evidence for neurone growth in animals closer to man, like the monkey.

Whether or not the ageing brain changes its structure, in some cases there do seem to be significant changes in the brain's chemistry, particularly in the neuro transmitters that act as the brain's chemical messengers. One of the most distressing ageing disorders caused by a disturbance in these transmitters is Parkinson's disease.

In the USA alone more than one million people suffer from this disease, in which the muscles become stiff and unco-ordinated. Most of these people are over 60, but each year thousands of much younger people become unemployed as a result of progressive disability caused by the disease. The sufferers' head and limbs shake; they find it difficult to start moving, but once started a walk can break into a run. Eating, speaking, dressing; anything that requires a moderate amount of muscle control becomes more and more difficult.

Since James Parkinson first described the symptoms in 1817,

scientists have failed to pinpoint the exact cause of the disease. What is known is that for some reason the disease only attacks a group of cells in the upper part of the brain. These cells contain a black pigment which gives the structure its name: the substantia nigra.

The cells of the substantia nigra form an important part of the brain's movement control centre. They help to fine-tune the body movements by keeping up an ongoing conversation with cells in another part of the movement centre, the basal ganglia. All of this communication is carried out via a chemical messenger called dopamine. Dopamine plays such an important part in the orchestration of movement that without it the thought of getting up out of a chair, or walking, cannot be translated into action.

In Parkinson's disease, the dopamine-producing cells in the substantia nigra gradually die off, cutting down the supply of dopamine and leading to jerky movements. As more and more brain cells die, less and less dopamine is released, and control of body movements becomes increasingly difficult.

It was an understanding of this chemical deficit that led to the development of a drug which was to transform the lives of many sufferers. This drug, called L Dopa, is converted into dopamine inside the body. Although at first it was thought L Dopa would cure Parkinson's disease once and for all, some sufferers were to find that even miracles have their price. Most patients find that L Dopa makes their life incomparably better, whatever stage of the disease they are at, but some unfortunate victims have to take the drug every two or three hours to regain control of their bodies and can suffer severe side effects like uncontrollable twitching. Ironically, these side effects appear to be the result of a dopamine 'overdose' because there is no way to control the amount of dopamine produced by L Dopa in the brain. There is also no way of diverting the extra dopamine to the areas of the brain where it is needed. Since Parkinson's is a progressive disease, L Dopa will never prevent the death of dopamine-producing cells and effect a 'cure' — but it will adjust the chemical balance so that some element of normality can be achieved, however fleetingly.

What would obviously be ideal would be to find a drug that would restore control of body movements without any side effects. But before any new drug can be developed scientists need to unravel the root cause of Parkinson's disease.

One theory is that the dopamine-producing cells are killed off by prolonged exposure to some sort of toxin or chemical in the environment. Over the last few years there has been intense scientific interest in the environmental toxin theory thanks to a bizarre discovery in California.

The story started in 1982 with the emergency admission of an unusual medical case; one of the prisoners at the local jail in San José had woken one morning to find that he could not move or talk. He was not a medical fluke: soon there was to be a sudden influx of young patients, all showing the sort of movement disorders normally seen in elderly Parkinson's patients. Even to neurologist William Langston, this was a difficult diagnosis to accept, since all the victims were young, healthy adults whose symptoms had appeared overnight. What his patients also had in common was an addiction to heroin. This was not so surprising; California is renowned throughout the world as a major drug centre, but in recent years a new trend had been established; drugs were turning up on the streets packaged and sold as heroin but artificially produced in makeshift laboratories. These synthetic versions of heroin were many times more powerful than heroin made from the opium poppy; their molecular structure had been manipulated to produce drugs that were purer, stronger and completely legal – legal because their esoteric composition was not pro-hibited under any law. These synthetic drugs were to become known in the drug underworld as 'designer drugs'.

It was a designer drug that caused the symptoms of Parkin-son's disease in the Californian patients. They had all used a synthetic heroin with a designer label on offer from a pusher in Northern California. As well as buying a 'high' they had also bought themselves a designer version of Parkinson's disease. Langston was at a loss to know how to treat his young addicts but eventually opted for L Dopa. The results were dramatic. Addicts who had been frozen into immobility started to move again. It was then that Langston realised their symptoms must be due to a lack of dopamine in their brains: somehow the process that normally took years to produce the symptoms of Parkinson's disease had been speeded up, and yet the implications of this were extraordinary; a substance contained in the designer heroin had travelled to the brain and destroyed only the dopamine-producing cells in the substantia nigra, leaving the rest of the brain unharmed. This was the sort of coincidence that scientists dream of; it was also the sort of human model of Parkinson's disease never before hoped for.

When scientists finally analysed the drug they found that it was contaminated with a chemical called MPTP, probably produced when this batch of designer drugs was carelessly stored in a hot garage. It was this contaminant that had struck down the addicts with Parkinson's disease.

Obviously, patients with normal Parkinson's disease have never taken designer drugs so MPTP in that form could not be the culprit, but they might at some stage have been exposed to an environmental toxin similar in structure and effect to MPTP. This environmental toxin theory of Parkinson's disease is controversial and has divided the scientific establishment. Its proponents argue that before symptoms of the disease develop, at least 80 per cent of the cells in the substantia nigra must have been destroyed. They believe that an environmental toxin initiates the whole process by destroying about half of all the cells in the substantia nigra and then normal ageing finishes the process off; once the 80 per cent reduction is reached, dopamine levels fall below a critical concentration and symptoms of the disease appear. This would mean that the ageing process has a small part to play in the evolution of Parkinson's disease, but only after the environmental toxin has caused the bulk of the damage.

Meanwhile, back in the lab, there was another unexpected twist in the story. Scientists working on MPTP discovered that on its own the chemical was harmless; the brain itself transformed MPTP into another, highly toxic, chemical that killed the cells in the substantia nigra. This toxin, called MPP+, seemed to be an unfortunate byproduct of the brain's waste disposal system. Normally, unwanted toxins are neutralised by a complex system of enzymes but when MPTP enters the brain for some reason the system has the reverse effect; by a quirk of nature MPTP is converted into lethal MPP+. The toxic properties of this chemical were already so well established that an American company had marketed it as a herbicide called Cyperquat.

The most obvious question was whether existing environmental herbicides could be related to the incidence of Parkinson's disease. A Canadian doctor decided to follow the incidence of Parkinson's disease in Quebec and discovered that the disease was not uniform, but varied across the nine different regions. It was highest in the agricultural region where pesticide use was common. This was not the only correlation. The five areas with the largest number of Parkinson's patients were all near pulp and paper mills. These results were intriguing, but by no means conclusive.

While the epidemiologists were trying to establish a link between environmental toxins and Parkinson's disease, a dramatic breakthrough was made. Scientists finally tracked down the enzyme responsible for the lethal transformation of MPTP to MPP+. The excitement increased when it was realised that this was a common enzyme called monoamine oxidase and there were already drugs in existence that could block its action.

Doctors in the United States and Canada have now combined in a huge 10 million dollar trial of one of these drugs in 28 centres across North America. This multicentre project will take about five years to complete and throughout that time up to 800 patients will be involved. William Langston has already started prescribing the drug to heroin addicts who took MPTP and some of them look as if they are improving. As well as being effective in human terms any successful drug will also be cost effective for society at large; the American team have estimated that the overall saving to society would exceed 10 million dollars every year if drug treatment could keep younger Parkinson's patients at work for just one extra week.

At the same time as the Federal Drug Administration gave permission for the new drug trial, scientists in Vancouver announced a technical breakthrough; they had developed a way of detecting Parkinson's disease before any symptoms appear. They used a machine called a positron emission tomography (PET) scanner to detect the areas of dopamine in the brain. The machine consists of a hollow core in which the patient is screened, not by X-rays or magnetic fields but by radiation emitted from the patient's own body. Before the scan, a radioactive form of sugar is injected into the blood-stream and passes to the brain where it is taken up by the cells. As it is used up, the radioactive glucose emits particles called positrons, which collide with electrons to produce gamma rays. Computers measure the radiation emitted and use it to build up photographs of sections of the brain. In a brain damaged by Parkinson's less of the radioactivity reaches the substantia nigra because the damaged cells are incapable of taking up the sugar. When Langston tested this technique on four of his young drug addicts who had used heroin contaminated by MPTP but had no symptoms, results from the PET scan showed early signs of brain damage. The damage was not as great as in patients with symptoms but it was there. Findings like these support the idea that damage to the cells in the substantia nigra develops slowly, and that symptoms will only appear when the damage has reached a maximum level in the final stages of destruction.

American doctors estimate that it costs at least 1,000 dollars for every patient who has a PET scan, so before the machine could be used in any sort of routine screening programme vast sums of money would have to be found. If that money was forthcoming then it is not beyond the realms of possibility for Parkinson PET scans to become as routine as ECGs for middle-aged men.

For those patients who already have Parkinson's disease and for whom these developments have come too late there is still a glimmer of hope; even their advanced brain damage might be reversed by using a technique that sounds more suited to the pages of a science-fiction novel than the inside of the operating theatre. At centres across the world scientists have been trying to treat the effects of Parkinson's disease by replacing the damaged parts of the brain with fresh dopamine-producing cells transplanted from a healthy donor brain.

Success in getting this recent brain-grafting technique to work hinged on the discovery that only brain tissue taken from an embryo would survive and grow. When monkeys with MPTP-induced Parkinson's disease were treated with brain grafts, 10 weeks after the operation their movements were almost back to normal. When the grafted tissue was examined under the microscope it showed that the transplanted cells were producing dopamine and had branched out to form new connections in the monkey's brain. It was thought this operation would never be able to be performed in Parkinson's patients because of insurmountable ethical problems, but then it was discovered that cells from another part of the body would work just as well. Cells in the adrenal gland, which sits on top of the kidney, have the same origins in the embryo as nerve cells in the brain. This means that under the right circumstances adrenal cells can be persuaded to make dopamine.

In 1982, this discovery led a group of surgeons at Stockholm's Karolinska Institute to attempt to treat older Parkinson's patients with their own adrenal tissue. This was an unprecedented experiment, but unfortunately, the results were disappointing and the technique abandoned. Then in March 1986 came the startling news from Mexico that several people suffering from Parkinson's disease had been cured by transplanting cells from the adrenal gland into their brains. The Mexican team had made a slight but perhaps important change to the Swedish procedure; they grafted tissue from the central part of the adrenal gland near to the substantia nigra but tucked inside a cavity in the brain where it would be bathed by nutrient cerebrospinal fluid. The results were unexpectedly good. One of the patients had been in a wheelchair before surgery; 10 months later he was farming and playing football. The Swedes thought the failure of their grafting experiments meant that the transplanted adrenal cells had not survived the operation. The Mexican scientists attributed their patients' dramatic improvement to the fact that their grafts had survived and were continuing to release dopamine into the brain. They also claimed that, as in the experiments carried out on monkeys, the donor cells were able to rebuild damaged connections in the Parkinson brain.

Scientists were not convinced by this explanation and thought it unlikely that such small grafts would lead to widespread restructuring over a large area of the brain.

A few weeks after the Mexicans announced their results, a US research team challenged the doubting Thomases in the medical community by starting their own transplant operations. In June 1987 the team released the results of operations carried out on six patients with Parkinson's disease. The report was cautious but encouraging. Two of the six patients had improved walking, balance and posture, while the team was still evaluating the other four. They found no evidence of increased dopamine in their patients after the transplant but suggested that the cells in the graft had released some other substance to achieve their effects. It is now thought that the brain itself might prepare the ground for receiving the new cells by surrounding the damaged neurones with tiny star-shaped cells which release a growth factor that helps the new cells settle in.

The idea that it might be possible to repair brain damage by transplantation has captured the imagination of the public and medical community alike. The list of Parkinson's patients waiting for the operation has increased dramatically. As far as the doctors and the public are concerned, brain transplants are hot stuff and many young researchers are now keen to work in this fast-moving field in the hope of finding the academic streets of medical research paved with gold. Since the Mexicans published their results, surgeons in at least five centres in the US and one in China have carried out adrenal operations. The operation is attracting its fair share of glamorous participants. One prospective patient is Muhammad Ali, the former world heavyweight boxing champion who now has Parkinson's disease. At the moment Ali controls his symptoms with L Dopa, but he has apparently told reporters that he is considering the operation.

While the Americans and the Mexicans pursue the effects of adrenal tissue transplants, the Swedes have gone a different route. They are concentrating on using human foetal brain tissue instead of adrenal cells and are coming to grips with the ethical minefield surrounding the use of aborted foetuses. They have already drawn up ethical guidelines to permit doctors to use foetal brain tissue under very controlled conditions, in which an ethical committee considers every case. So far the research team have successfully transplanted human cells into rats using a drug which prevents the new cells from being rejected. It now looks as it the Swedes are well on the way to performing their brain cell transplants in patients. So far the results are extremely encouraging, but it is too soon to know whether grafting tissue from the adrenal gland or from the foetus is an effective treatment for Parkinson's disease.

As for the designer drug victims who unlocked the door to the cause and effects of this debilitating disease, there is no immediate cure. Perhaps one day they will be offered brain transplants to treat their specialised form of Parkinson's disease but for the moment they linger in institutions across California, aware that their starring role in the Parkinson's story has brought hope to millions of sufferers but turned them into human guinea pigs.

The prospect of regenerating the brain by cell transplants has caused immense excitement among scientists studying other degenerative brain disorders such as Alzheimer's disease. Alzheimer's used to be regarded as a sad but natural consequence of getting older. For many years it was believed that if we lived long enough we would all succumb to this form of dementia. It is now known that Alzheimer's is not a part of normal ageing and that like Parkinson's disease it is due to a particular kind of damage to one area of the brain. It is recognized as a specific disease, quite distinct from any of the effects of normal ageing. As such scientists have been trying to unravel its causes in the hope of finding ways to prevent, and in the long term cure, this devastating condition.

Many doctors now think Alzheimer's may be genetically inherited, but that the pattern of inheritance is difficult to spot because the victims' ancestors do not always live long enough to develop the disease. It starts by attacking the mind. One of the first symptoms of the disease is loss of memory: names, faces and dates; the contents of a whole life start to drift out of reach. Simple tasks learned long ago like making a cup of tea, turning on the light or telling the time become too complicated to remember. As the disease progresses patients lose more and more of their past. The difference between this sort of memory loss and that of normal ageing has been described as the difference between forgetting where you left your glasses, and forgetting that you even wear them.

Once the mind starts to deteriorate, the disease begins to attack the body; control over bodily functions is lost, eventually leaving the victim totally dependent on family and friends. As the disease tightens its grip the biological clock reverses until the Shakespearean vision of old age is fulfilled and the victim regresses into second childhood, 'sans teeth, sans eyes, sans taste, sans everything'. Total breakdown of the mind and body takes anywhere between six and twenty years.

With an ever growing ageing population the disease is on the increase and will affect an estimated one and three-quarter million people in the United Kingdom by 1995 if it remains unchecked. The same pattern is reflected in the US; it is thought that two and a half million Americans already suffer from the condition, 40 per cent of whom are already in nursing homes. Those figures are expected to jump at least 50 per cent in the next decade and with 120,000 people dying of the disease every year the need for an effective treatment has become a matter of urgency.

A German neurologist called Alois Alzheimer first named the disease in 1907. He described the case of a 51-year-old woman who had displayed 'progressive jealousy' and died four years later after severe dementia. A post mortem revealed two abnormalities in her brain, the first of which was a plaque, a round area that was made up of degenerating brain cells. The second abnormality, never before described, was called a neurofibrillary tangle, and consisted of abnormal brain cells. These plaques and tangles were concentrated in areas of the brain mainly concerned with memory and personality. Unlike Parkinson's disease, Alzheimer's has no effect on the movement areas of the brain. Alzheimer's observations were to prove very important; there is no simple diagnostic test for the disease, the only way to be sure is to examine the brain tissue either after the patient dies or by removing part of the brain while the patient is still alive.

While plaques and tangles are found in normal ageing brains, only in the Alzheimer's patient do they infiltrate the brain to such an extent. Why abnormal amounts of plaques and tangles should be formed in Alzheimer's disease has never been discovered. Scientific observations have concentrated on microscopic examination of the complex composition of the abnormal tangles, particularly the filaments from which they are formed. Inside normal nerve cells these filaments are used to form a kind of cell skeleton. This skeleton acts like the cell's microscopic equivalent of bone and muscle and is responsible for moving the cell around, for positioning things inside it and for cell division. The proteins that make up this skeleton are slightly different in different types of cells but they are all very tough and resistant to attack. As well as establishing the backbone of the cell, the cytoskeleton acts like a postal service, moving proteins made inside the nerve cell out to its nerve branches.

In Alzheimer's disease this skeleton breaks down and the filaments twist around each other in a characteristic way. Because these filaments are so tough the cell's natural waste disposal enzymes cannot digest them and they get transported, along with normal proteins, out of the cell to the nerve terminals. Because these plaques and tangles are laid down in dying neurones, they can be used as markers of dead or dying cells in the Alzheimer brain, but the underlying processes that lead to their formation remained a mystery, until the spring of 1987, when it seemed that American researchers had found the answer. Within the same week four separate groups reported the isolation and characterisation of a gene involved with Alzheimer's disease, and a fifth group from Boston announced the discovery of a genetic 'marker' associated with the disease.

The uncovering of a genetic marker reinforced the feeling that a gene is responsible for a particular type of Alzheimer's called familial Alzheimer's disease. As the name suggests, this disease runs in families. It is slightly different to the more common form in that it comes on at an earlier age and its progress is very rapid; some family members are struck down by the disease in their early forties and are completely taken over by it within just a few years. Luckily it is fairly rare and only accounts for about 10 per cent of all Alzheimer's victims, but these findings had a much wider implication because many scientists believed that even the more common form of Alzheimer's had a genetic component. The scientists identified the marker on the chromosome known as number 21 out of the 23 pairs found inside every cell. They decided to look at this particular chromosome because it is responsible for the genetic defect that leads to Down's syndrome. Down's sufferers have three copies of chromosome 21, rather than the usual two. The link with Alzheimer's disease is that victims of Down's syndrome who survive to the age of 35 or older have the same sorts of brain abnormalities.

The American researchers studied four international families with an unusually high risk of Alzheimer's; one Italian family had 48 members afflicted with the disease over eight generations. In their search to find a genetic link, the scientists studied medical records from an Italian mental asylum, where diseased members of the family had been left to die, supposedly insane. Eventually this sort of detective work paid off and the team homed in on a stretch of chromosome 21 that included about 500 genes, one of which presumably causes Alzheimer's disease.

Meanwhile, the Boston research team had located, also on chromosome 21, the gene responsible for making the protein that forms the middle of the Alzheimer plaques. This finding caused great excitement because it seemed reasonable to suppose that the gene that was responsible for familial Alzheimer's was the same gene that produced the protein inside the plaques. This would mean that Alzheimer's was caused by a particular gene producing too much protein or even an abnormal protein which was then deposited in the brain where it would lead to the characteristic symptoms of the disease. Excitement soon gave way to disappointment when it was discovered a few months later that the genes were not one and the same and that protein was laid down in the abnormal plaques after the disease had already started; it appeared to be an effect rather than a cause.

As well as tangles and plaques forming in the Alzheimer brain, as in Parkinson's disease there is also a marked reduction in one of the brain's chemical messengers. In this case the culprit is not dopamine but acetylcholine. In the past few years, three separate British research teams have made the same finding; the brains of victims of Alzheimer's disease show an abnormally low level of an enzyme responsible for the manufacture of acetylcholine, one of the brain's chief neurotransmitters. No one really knows why this happens; it may be that the cells containing the enzyme actually die out, or that while the cells survive they lose the ability to make the enzyme.

Just like the early work on memory, attempts to correct the acetylcholine imbalance in Alzheimer's patients met with little success. Patients were fed choline and lecithin, the starting ingredients from which acetylcholine is made in the brain, in the vain hope that more of the transmitter would be synthesized. It is now known that that approach would never have succeeded because for some reason, young patients with Alzheimer's synthesise less acetylcholine even when their diet is rich in choline and lecithin.

A second approach was tried. This time the idea was to increase the amount of acetylcholine present by using a drug that prevents it being broken down in the brain. The drug, called tetrahydroaminoacridine (THA), ws given to a group of elderly patients who suffered from moderate to severe Alzheimer's disease.

These results were much more encouraging. After only three weeks patients performed better in memory tests and by the end of the first year there were striking changes in everyday behaviour; one patient was able to do the housework, another went back to work part time and a retired patient took up golf again. Even patients with the more advanced form of the disease were able to feed themselves again.

Despite this initial success the doctor who carried out these trials has emphasised that THA is no more a cure for Alzheimer's disease than L Dopa is for Parkinson's disease. Two of the patients deteriorated in spite of the drug because it was not able to stop the continuing progress of the disease. What THA can do is alleviate symptoms at any given stage and perhaps allow patients to experience a few more years of relatively normal life.

Apart from a drug to cure Alzheimer's disease, in the future it might be possible to use the same brain-grafting techniques for Alzheimer's patients as those now being used with some success in treating Parkinson's disease. However, it is an approach that is fraught with scientific and ethical problems. At the moment the only successful grafting technique for Parkinson's patients uses cells taken from the patient's own adrenal gland to release dopamine into the brain. However, there is no equivalent organ in the body that can be exploited to produce acetylcholine, so the only way to repair faulty acetylcholine neurones is to replace them with healthy brain cells from a human foetus. As with Parkinson's disease, this means the same moral and ethical fences have to be climbed.

Even if foetal cells could be used, there is no guarantee of success. The changes that lead to the damage in Alzheimer's disease are so widespread in the brain that it is difficult to see how a simple grafting experiment could work. The prospects for success with this approach will probably be clearer when the team of Swedish doctors go ahead with plans to graft human cells into the brains of Parkinson's patients.

Along with acetylcholine there are other important brain transmitters implicated in Alzheimer's disease. One of these is an amino acid (the building blocks of protein) called glutamate. For some reason the receptors for glutamate in the brain of an Alzheimer's victim are far too sensitive. This sort of heightened sensitivity to a brain transmitter seems to happen when the usual supply of the chemical has been cut off or reduced in some way so the receptor tries to compensate by becoming even more receptive. It has been argued that if the supersensitivity of the glutamate receptors is due to a reduction in levels of glutamate, this deficiency could be yet another cause of the patient's symptoms. If glutamate levels in the brain could be increased, symptoms of the disease could at least be controlled.

This interest in glutamate has led to the discovery of a new drug which, although in the long term might lead to such a treatment for Alzheimer's disease, in the immediate future is offering hope to millions of sufferers from another con-sequence of old age — cerebral stroke.

In simple terms there are really only two kinds of stroke. First there is the brain's version of a heart attack: fatty deposits narrow the arteries of the brain (just as they do in the coronary arteries of the heart) so that if a blood clot forms it can effectively block off the narrowed artery. The area of the brain that has its blood supply interrupted dies. The second and most serious form of stroke happens when a blood vessel ruptures and the haemorrhage floods nearby parts of the brain. Only about one in ten strokes occur in this way, but 80 per cent of them are fatal.

Although during a stroke cells in the brain are deprived of blood, it is now thought that they do not die just because the lack of blood has starved them of oxygen, but because they become over-sensitive to glutamate when the blood supply is restored. This surge of glutamate causes the cells to fire off messages far too rapidly so they eventually burn out and die. One way to limit this sort of damage is to block the glutamate receptors after a stroke so that when the glutamate does reach the cells, very little can get inside and have such a devastating effect.

The pharmaceutical company Merck, Sharp and Dohme have just developed a drug, code-named MK 801 which in animal experiments seems to do just that. The Food and Drug Administration has now approved MK 801 for initial clinical testing in the United States and Merck, Sharp and Dohme are testing tolerance to injected doses of the drug in a small group of volunteers. Unlike Alzheimer's disease, there are really no good alternative drug treatments for stroke patients so any new approach that could produce even a small improvement would be welcomed.

Although there is no real cure at present for patients with Alzheimer's or stroke victims, there is the prospect of treatment and for those at risk there may even be the hope of prevention. For the majority of the elderly, unthreatened by disease, there is just a coming to terms with the consequences of normal ageing which may include a change in mental agility.

This process of slowing down can be affected by the degree of stimulation in our external environment, and the way that we react to that environment. As we saw in Chapter Four, too much stress can have a damaging effect not only on the immune system, but also on the brain. American scientists are studying the effects of hormones called glucocorticoids which are released by the adrenal gland whenever we are faced with a stressful situation. Too much stress causes large amounts of glucocorticoids to be released, which at high levels can interfere with the ability of the brain cell to store energy; this starts a general decline that ends in the death of the cell.

This is certainly the case with rats, but to find out if it applied to the sort of social stress that human beings endure the scientists turned to the baboon. The population they chose lived in a National Park in East Africa. Every year one of the baboons was captured and its body's response to stress measured. To work out what sort of social stresses the animals were normally subjected to, the physiological results were matched with the baboon's status in the group. Baboons, it seems, are just as status-conscious as humans, so in terms of baboon society it is possible to be high ranking, low ranking or just middle of the baboon road. The results reinforce our own competitive standards in that it is not only more satisfying but also healthier to be top of the heap even if you are a baboon; top-ranking baboons had the most efficient and therefore the healthiest stress response.

It is still not known whether the glucocorticoids released during stress can damage human brain cells, but if the animal experiments bear any relationship to the way we respond to our environment then it might be worth trying to protect ourselves; not necessarily by becoming the top baboon but by learning to relax and adopting a more positive approach to life. The trick is to get the balance right, because scientists have now discovered that too little stress can be just as harmful as too much.

It has been known for some time that when young rats are removed from a dull, uninteresting cage and put into an exciting environment they form new brain connections, but it was always thought that old rats would not be able to respond in the same way. To test this a group of American scientists decided to recreate in rat terms the sort of dull, humdrum existence that a human can experience by keeping rats in solitary confinement in a small cage. When the rats reached old age they were placed in the rat's equivalent of Disneyland to see what effect this would have on their brains.

The new cages contained lots of puzzles and toys designed to entice even the most lethargic of the rodent species. When the elderly rats arrived in this environment they at first used the toys to hide under but as their confidence grew they gradually began to explore and to socialise with one another. After a time they started to play with their toys. As they became more active these elderly, overweight rats started to lose weight and become more agile, but the effect of the experience on their brains was far more startling.

In one region of the brain the rats had formed over 2,000 new connections between the nerve cells. These connections allowed the rats to process new information in the brain, almost in the form of a new memory. The rats that had been left to grow old in boredom had very limited numbers of connections left in the brain. It was almost as if the brain cells had withered away because there was no new experience to stimulate their growth.

This research suggests that not only does the brain have the ability to form new connections between its cells to incorporate new information, but that this process can be actively encouraged by a stimulating environment. Mental exercise, like physical exercise, is needed to produce a healthy brain.

The wish to be open to new situations and to cope with challenges distinguishes people whose mental awareness grows during old age. Even if work is no longer a possibility then retirement itself can be made a time of new experience. Some retirement communities have been designed to make use of the new research and deliberately make physical and intellectual demands on the ageing residents. They provide an environment where the elderly can continue to learn, develop and adapt because the ageing brain will grow and change in response to new information. Elderly people who stay involved in the world around them, who continue with intellectual interests, and who have a flexible attitude to life are the people who are most likely to stay mentally alert.

Ageing will always be a time of slowing down and gradual decline, but the speed of that decline is in many ways under our own control. The key to successful ageing seems to lie with the individual; exercising the brain should keep it younger longer, and providing it with a rich and varied day-to-day environment will prevent the rapid loss of vital brain cells. The most important advances that are within reach are surgical and pharmacological treatments for the ageing diseases of Parkinson's, Alzheimer's and stroke, and the understanding that for the healthy individual, normal ageing could be just a state of mind.

CHAPTER SIX

Papering the Cracks

The most obvious signs of ageing appear on the face, a simple fact of life that has been exploited for years by those embarrassingly accurate fairground acts which promise to 'guess your age'. In just the same way we scan each others' faces for the trademarks of ageing. We search out wrinkles and lines, drooping eyelids and flabby chins, grey hairs and receding hairlines. Almost subconsciously we run through the mental checklist which enables us to estimate someone's age.

If we want to appear younger than we are, we have to alter these visual clues. We have to hunt out disguises which are to old age what false moustaches were to Sherlock Holmes. It is exactly this which is the aim of the cosmetic industry. They do not try to slow the fundamental process of ageing in the body as a whole. Instead they simply try to hide or prevent its most obvious effects. They cannot provide youthful vigour, but they can offer a morale-building facsimile of the real thing. They don't hold out the promise of immortality, but at least you can die without a double chin.

Business is booming, and likely to carry on expanding, since, as we saw earlier, it is estimated that by 1990 60 per cent of the population of Western Europe and the US will be over 60 years of age. So great is the potential of anti-ageing potions, no cosmetics company can afford to be without its own anti-ageing remedy.

The front line in the cosmetics business is the skin – and skin does much more than simply hold us together. In fact it is one of the largest organs in the body, accounting for about one-eighth of the weight of a normal individual. It is a vital barrier which prevents toxic chemicals and harmful organisms from entering our bodies; it also prevents fatal dehydration by limiting the amount of water that escapes from the body; it plays a vital role in regulating the body temperature and, because it is jam-packed with nerve endings, it allows us to feel with every part of our body. It helps to protect against damage from harmful ultraviolet light, and at the same time uses light to trigger the body's synthesis of vitamin D.

Under most circumstances the damage that everyday living causes to our skin is permanent and cumulative. This makes it difficult to separate out the effects of wear and tear from the ravages of the intrinsic ageing process, but it appears that much of the damage we think of as being caused by old age is really due to weathering of some sort – particularly too much exposure to the sun. All recent research shows that the way the skin bears up under the onslaught of time has as much to do with how it is treated as with age.

To understand what cosmetics can and cannot offer, we have to understand the way that nature has designed what is in effect an immensely complicated overcoat. The top layer of the skin is called the epidermis. In most places on the body it is less than a millimetre thick, although it is thicker on our backs, and thicker still on the soles of our feet and the palms of our hands. There are no blood vessels running through it; instead it consists almost exclusively of stacked layers of cells.

Below the epidermis, and separated from it by a thin membrane, lies the second layer of the skin, the dermis. This is a much thicker layer, varying between two and four millimetres in depth, and rather than having a cellular structure like the epidermis, it is made up of a dense felt-work of connective tissue in which bundles of collagen fibres intermingle with a mesh of elastic tissue. The dermis contains the hair follicles, the sweat glands and the sebaceous glands, which secrete a waxy, oily lubricant called sebum. Unlike the epidermis, the dermis has a complement of blood vessels, nerves, and lymphatics.

Beneath the dermis lies a layer which is the sworn enemy of all slimmers, the hypodermis. The hypodermis is where we put on weight because sitting among the fibres of connective tissue are masses of sleek and oily fat cells. When we eat more food than we need to, our body converts the excess into fat and stores it in these cells, which expand like plumped-up cushions under the skin. This fat store acts like an emergency fuel tank, and also provides some extra thermal insulation for the body, which is why fat people tend to survive the longest in extreme cold.

The epidermis and dermis have different but vital functions. The epidermis is the front line, the physical barrier which protects the body, while the dermis provides a tough flexible layer which the epidermis can cling to during even the most violent bodily contortions.

The epidermis goes about its task in a subtle and complex way. From the time this layer develops in the embryo until the time an individual dies, the epidermis continually manufactures fresh cells to replace those shed from the skin through the wear and tear of everyday life. This factory production of new epidermal cells is mainly carried out by cells at the base of the epidermis, the basal cells which now feature in more and more skin-care advertisements. Once a new cell has been produced it starts on a two to three week migration towards the skin's surface to replace the cells that are being shed. It is during this journey that the cell undergoes profound changes which are vital in determining what skin-care products can and cannot do.

The most important change is that the cell is 'keratinized', keratin being a term used to describe the family of proteins that make up nails, claws, hooves and hair. As you would expect from the material that forms fingernails, keratin is insoluble and generally highly resistant to chemical attack. During keratinization the cell slowly dies, and its interior is gradually filled with a web of keratin fibres. The cell also becomes progressively flatter as it travels towards the surface of the skin and the cell's outer membrane hardens via the process of cross-linking which we looked at in Chapter Two.

The result of these changes is that the surface of the epidermis, the stratum corneum, is made up of dead, hardened cells which because of their flatness lock tightly together and form a highly effective barrier against substances trying to enter or leave the body. To give added efficiency, the sebum produced by the sebaceous glands in the dermis rises to the surface and spreads over the stratum corneum. This oily, waxy layer helps bind the dead cells together, keeping the stratum corneum flexible and adding to its impermeability. The slight stickiness of the sebum allows us to perform delicate manipulations with a minimum of finger pressure.

Within the basal layer of the epidermis there are large numbers of triangular cells studded with fine, branching arms. These are the melanocytes, cells which play a vital role in protecting the body from the harmful effects of ultraviolet radiation. The human body contains about two billion of these cells, distributed throughout the body, mostly in the epidermis, the hair and the eyes.

The melanocytes manufacture the skin pigment melanin, the red-black chemical which is responsible for the colour of the skin and hair, and which filters out some of the harmful ultraviolet rays of the sun. When we expose ourselves to a lot of sun, our bodies produce more melanin, and the net result is a suntan. However, melanin does not filter out all of the ultraviolet light, and even a deep tan allows a substantial amount of harmful ultraviolet light to pass deep into the dermis.

Although the epidermis is what goes on display to the outside world, the tough, resilient dermis underneath it does far more to determine our appearance than the epidermis ever can. The dermis makes up the bulk of our skin. It comprises a three-dimensional network of collagen fibres interwoven with fibres of another protein called elastin. The collagen gives skin its strength, the elastin its elasticity. This whole lattice work is embedded in a gel (or 'ground substance') which carries nutrients and hormones from the blood vessels to the various cells which are also dotted throughout the dermis.

The main function of the dermis is mechanical. When we are young the collagen bundles in the dermis are neatly organised into a lattice work. The collagen fibres, which form about 30 per cent of the volume of the dermis, have tremendous strength, but very little elasticity. In fact they are so strong it is reckoned that each collagen fibre can support at least 10,000 times its own weight. Although the individual fibres cannot stretch, just as a trellis work hinged at every joint will respond to being pulled in a particular direction, the overall network can extend in the direction in which a particular piece of skin is being stretched. When the stretching stops the network is pulled back into place by the rubber-like elastin fibres which are laced throughout the collagen network. Elastin molecules have a haphazard coiled structure which straightens out when it is pulled and then springs back, rather like a twisted coil of rubber. Unlike rubber, the elastin is not particularly strong, but the interwoven collagen fibres set a limit to the amount of stretching, and so prevent the elastin from tearing. The only time tearing is commonly seen is during pregnancy or during rapidly developing obesity when it produces 'stretch marks'.

Wrinkling is the most obvious effect of ageing on the skin. It starts during our twenties and gets progressively worse with age. First there are the deep lines produced by different facial expressions like smiling and frowning. We rely on our faces to communicate a vast range of human emotion, but there is a price to be paid. Lines form in the areas of greatest movement and deepen as the years go by. Every emotion, from laughter to rage, is gradually recorded on our faces.

The first lines to develop are usually 'frown lines' across the forehead; these record the movement of the muscle which sweeps up from each eyebrow to the hairline and allows us to raise our eyebrows and the skin on the forehead. This is closely followed by the appearance of wrinkles that radiate fanwise from the corners of our eyes. Known for centuries as 'crows' feet', the more prominent middle one is often called the 'over-forty line'. Other facial wrinkles develop on the upper and lower eyelids, and two vertical or comma-shaped frown lines develop on either side of the root of the nose. The play of expression around the mouth, especially smiling, produces deep grooves running between the nose and the mouth. It can also produce an equally deep groove extending downwards from the mouth to the chin. These lines develop in the fifties and get deeper and deeper.

To add insult to injury, during the fifties two prominent lines start moving up the neck, following the line of the platysma muscle, a muscle which extends from below the collar bone to the angle of the jaw, allowing us to pull down the corner of the mouth. By the time we reach our sixties we may be getting past the point of caring because by then we can also expect to see multiple fine lines radiating outwards from the edge of our lips, rather like the folding produced by the tightening of a purse string, due to the muscle which closes and compresses the lips.

Other ageing changes alter the appearance of the face, particularly in relation to the eyes. Puffiness, especially below the lower lids, develops in the forties and fifties because fat is squeezed into the area, and there is a certain amount of unwanted fluid retention. Much later on the process almost goes into reverse and the eyes appear sunken because fat is lost from the orbit, the cavity in the skull that holds the eye.

Age also brings a more insidious wrinkling process. All over the body the skin starts to lose its firmness and its elasticity, so that it sags in accordance with the law of gravity rather than clinging to the contours of the body. Perhaps the most obvious example of this is when sagging neck tissues combine with fat deposition to produce the dreaded double chin.

The loss of fat from the fuel reserve can also cause wrinkling, and is the main reason for the characteristic emaciated look of very old people with hands, for example, prominently display-ing every bone, tendon, and blood vessel. This is not life threatening, but there are more serious implications. This loss of fatty padding means that there is nothing between bones and the skin, and explains why elderly people are plagued by the problem of pressure sores. This loss of insulation also makes older people much more vulnerable to death from hypo-thermia, or very low body temperature. Older people are also far more likely to have dry, cracked skin. This is not only uncomfortable, but also opens the skin up to attack by bac-teria, viruses and fungi. This is why elderly people are far more likely to suffer from skin infections.

If we are going to slow down or prevent these developments we have to delve into the subtle and complex changes which overtake the skin with everyday use and increasing age. It is important to remember (as well as being good for morale) that many of the features which are meant to signify old age have as much to do with how you have treated your skin as with any intrinsic ageing process. Nevertheless, there are some clear trends which can be put down to increasing age.

The epidermis starts to become much thinner, so that our

skin starts to take on a transparent, paper-like appearance. There are also important changes within this layer. From youth onwards, and particularly after the age of 50, the epidermal production line starts to slow down, and quality control seems to go out of the window, with individual cells varying enormously in shape and size. Overall, age brings a shrinkage in the volume of these cells, and if you take skin samples from an area which has not been exposed to wind and sun, you find that their size is directly related to age.

The slowing of the cell production line could be genetically programmed, or it could be that damage by ultraviolet light and chemicals is to blame. What is clear is that in old age the epidermis is no longer well structured and tightly layered. Gaps in the increasingly disorganised structure become filled with fluid and the epidermis may collapse, leading to the smaller wrinkles that appear on older faces. This 'cratering' is particularly noticeable in areas where the epidermis is very thin, such as around the eye.

The stratum corneum, the layer of dead, horny cells on the surface of the epidermis, also changes with the passing years. The number of cells that are shed drops sharply with increasing age, paralleling the lower production of fresh cells in the epidermis. The cells also become much flatter, probably because with increasing age it takes them much longer to travel from the basal layer to the skin's surface. These differences probably produce subtle alterations in the appearance of the skin, in particular its reflectivity, helping to explain why, with age, skin starts to lose its sheen.

It seems that the water content of the stratum corneum falls with age, and this could explain why superficial fissuring occurs in the skin of the elderly when it is inflamed. One reason for this may have to do with the sebaceous glands. Although their number remains relatively constant, the amount of sebum they produce decreases throughout adult life with the result that there is less of this oily substance to slick down the stratum corneum and add some final waterproofing.

The number of melanocytes decreases by somewhere between eight and 20 per cent every 10 years, particularly after the age of 30. Their increasing scarcity leads to the irregular mottled pigmentation often seen in older people and explains why older people find it more difficult to tan as deeply or as evenly as young people. The melanocytes which do remain tend to gather in the areas which are habitually exposed to the sun.

Like the epidermis, the dermis also becomes thinner with the passing years. The dermis accounts for 95 per cent of the thickness of skin – when we measure the thickness of skin we are mainly measuring the dermis. Ultrasound measurements show that skin thickness gradually increases up to the age of 20; it then stays constant until the age of about 40, before dropping into a steady decline. Not only does the dermis feel thinner, it also looks less substantial and may allow veins, muscles and tendons to be more easily seen. On the whole the dermis is thicker in men than in women, which may be one contributory factor to the perception that female skin deteriorates with age faster than male skin.

Another important factor that alters our looks with age was first noticed by P. Lacompte du Nouy, a French military surgeon in World War One. During that war he became intrigued by the way in which the body heals wounds, and he continued with his research into this subject long after the conflict was finished. In 1937 he published a paper reporting that in a 20-year-old man a 40 centimetre wound could close in approximately 40 days, but in a 40-year-old man it took around 76 days. More recent studies produce the same conclusion: we aren't as good at healing wounds (whether from accidents or surgery) as we get older. At first sight this may seem to have little to do with how our skin looks as we age, but in fact there is an important connection. The underlying reason for the slower repair rates in elderly people is that the fibroblasts (the cells which manufacture collagen and elastin) decrease in number and size with age. This means that the process of replacing existing collagen and elastin fibres slows down with age, and so damage tends to accumulate. That damage will show itself to the world in our faces.

Both the collagen and elastin undergo great changes with age. To a certain extent these changes are driven by an intrinsic ageing process, because they still take place in skin which has been completely protected from the outside world. However the main factors are environmental: chemicals, pollutants and above all the ultraviolet part of the sun's spectrum. Sunbathing, more than any other factor, is responsible for ageing our skin.

As the years pass two processes start to work on the collagen fibres. First, increased chemical bonding in the form of cross-linking starts to take place between the individual strands of the collagen fibre. This stiffens the fibre and makes it more resistant to chemical attack, which is why many dermatologists refer to it as 'insoluble collagen'. At first sight tougher cables of collagen seem a bonus, but unfortunately there is a drawback. In younger collagen the chemical sites on the collagen strands which will later cross-link bind instead to water, giving the young collagen fibre an amazing ability to absorb moisture, and plump out the dermis to hide any irregularities. Once this ability is lost any bumps and hollows in the dermis are bared to the world. The water bound into the collagen dermis will no longer be able to conceal the lines. Folds caused in the dermis by our facial expressions will be reflected in the epidermis and we will start to see wrinkles.

However, as more time passes this process is overtaken by an even more destructive one: the collagen fibres start to fragment, and the entire collagen network starts to disintegrate. The consequences are dire. As we have seen, young skin is firm and elastic because it can rely on the elastin fibres to always snap the supporting collagen network back into place. When this network falls apart, there is no structure for the elastin to pull on, and so the dermis sags with gravity. It finishes by resembling a bag of jelly filled with isolated strands of collagen and elastin.

To make matters worse the elastin fibres themselves are not immune to the effects of age. They become more irregularly distributed, and the fibres become more ragged and susceptible to dissociation by enzyme attack. Overall the amount of elastin in the dermis starts to fall. These changes are far more noticeable in persons aged between 50 and 70 than they are in people aged 30 to 50 (assuming that no one in the younger group has had a high degree of exposure to sunlight).

There are also changes in the ground substance, the gel which fills the gaps between the collagen and elastin. As the dermis ages the hyaluronic acid content of the ground substance decreases. Hyaluronic acid is a chemical which allows the ground substance to hold enormous amounts of water. The more water held within it, the plumper, more stretched, more elastic and fine in texture the skin will be. The decrease in hyaluronic acid with age may lead to a change in the stickiness of the ground substance so that the dermis becomes less plump and firm.

The blood vessels in the dermis become smaller in cross-section and the rate of blood flow decreases. This is one more reason why older people tend to feel the cold more. It probably also contributes to the loss of colour in the face with age. Rosy cheeks and the bloom of youth are replaced by a pale, washed-out pallor. The epidermis has no blood vessels, and is supplied with oxygen and nutrients by tiny tubes which loop upwards from the blood vessels of the dermis to the junction with the epidermis. With age there is a striking reduction in the number of these tubes and the epidermis is not kept nearly so well supplied with nutrients.

Although these changes will occur in even the most protected skin, there is no doubt that the doses of ultraviolet light that we get from the sun are the major factor in accelerating them. The melanin in our skin will filter out some of the ultraviolet light, but it will not be able to cope with the scorching levels encountered during a serious bout of sunbathing.

Ultraviolet light characteristically produces free radicals (see Chapter Two) when it encounters complex organic chemicals, and these free radicals are capable of causing enormous damage to the epidermis and dermis – especially as most free radical reactions are chain reactions. Some of these free radicals will damage the collagen directly. Others will initiate changes which disrupt the delicate chemical balance within the dermis and lead to the release of enzymes which can digest the collagen fibres. Letting loose free radicals among the delicate chemical architecture of the dermis is equivalent to firing a shotgun in a china shop.

Under the microscope, skin from someone who has exposed their skin to large doses of sunlight shows an enormous amount of damage. Instead of an organised network of collagen and elastin fibres there are irregular clumps and strands –

what dermatologists call the 'spaghetti and meatball' appearance. In very severely affected areas virtually the whole upper dermis, and perhaps even the middle of the dermis, will be abnormal. Sun tanning quickly achieves the same effect as years of ageing. Ultraviolet light also affects the epidermis; it devastates the internal architecture of the cells leaving an assortment of strange, twisted cells which are thought to play an important part in the development of skin cancer.

So, to prevent time placing its footprints all over our faces, one of the most important things we can do is to cut down the amount of ultraviolet light that we allow to fall on our skin. The sun's ultraviolet radiation (UVR) is arbitrarily divided into three segments – UVA, UVB and UVC.

Very little UVC even reaches the earth's surface because most of it is filtered out by the ozone layer and the atmosphere below. The bulk of the damage to skin is caused by UVB. Until recently it was thought that UVA caused little damage to skin and certainly you need 1,000 times as much of it to cause the same amount of sunburn as UVB. However recent experiments have shown that even though UVA may not cause suntan it can cause lasting damage to the dermis.

The first step in preventing UVR damage must be to change our attitude to the sun tan. Tropical beaches and sunbeds do nothing for the health of the skin. Although sunbeds irradiate the body with very low levels of UVR, there is growing evidence that low doses can cause just as much damage as higher doses. The UVR levels on a beach are incredibly high, because as well as direct exposure to the sun, you also have to contend with the UVR that is reflected off the water and the sand. A two-week holiday in the sun leads to a UVR dose that is around three times what someone living in the UK gets over the rest of the year. That is one reason why there is currently an explosion in the number of skin cancer patients in the UK. UVR levels are also extremely high on ski slopes. This is because there is more UVR at altitude together with decreased diffusion by clouds and higher reflectivity from the white snow.

We need to shift our taste back towards the Victorian ideal of protecting the skin at all times, and reassess the associations we have formed between sun tans and health. Parasols on the beach may soon be back in vogue. Even though a tanned skin is less likely to burn, exposure to large doses of sunlight still allows UVR to penetrate into the dermis. In white Caucasians it is now generally accepted that skin damage due to UV light occurs whatever the level of tanning.

The cosmetics industry has in recent years come up with many highly efficient sunscreens designed to absorb or reflect UVR. Older products like red veterinary jelly and zinc oxide are highly effective but extremely obvious, so the industry has had to come up with products which are more cosmetically acceptable. In addition these products must cling to the skin surface for at least one hour after application and resist being washed or scrubbed off. Most of the sunscreens that are sold in the shops at the moment concentrate on absorbing UVB. Their efficiency in doing this is expressed as a Sunburn Protection Factor or SPF. This is the ratio of the minimum time it takes for artificial UVR to produce sunburn to the time required without protection. Most sunscreens have SPFs between four and 15.

However, because of the damage that UVA can cause, sunscreens which filter out only UVB are not very useful because they may end up increasing our UVA dose: if you are able to spend long hours in the sun without fear of burning from the UVB you will accumulate far higher doses of UVA than would otherwise be possible. Sunscreens based on benzophenones and also anthranilates will absorb UVA, but there is still a need for broader protection, to include wavelengths which are not sufficiently filtered out by any of the products currently on the shelves.

Sunscreens do not have to be confined to the beach. As the vital role played by UVR in skin ageing becomes better known, more and more cosmetic companies are adding sunscreens to their everyday products so that skin can be given continual protection. There is general agreement that using sunscreens in this way will significantly cut the speed at which wrinkles and lines start to form. If you want to keep your skin young, stay out of the sun and always use a sunscreen.

There is another compelling reason to use sunscreens. Skin cancer is currently increasing at a phenomenal rate, matching our love affair with the sun tan. UVR causes disarray inside the cells of the epidermis, and can alter them to such an extent that they become cancerous. It also cuts down the number of Langerhans cells in the skin, cells which play a vital role in the immune system of the skin – including the role of identifying and destroying carcinogenic cells. These changes also occur in the skin through the natural process of ageing, but UVR accelerates their progress to a tremendous extent. Furthermore the older we get, the fewer melanocytes we have, and the more UVR penetrates through to the epidermis and the dermis.

If you still want a tan there are chemicals which will let you achieve one with only minimal exposure to the rays of the sun. The chemical dihydroxyacetone, for example, seems to react with amino acids in the skin to produce a similar colour to suntan – although this artificial tan is purely cosmetic and gives no protection from sun burn. There are also chemicals called psoralens which if eaten produce a suntan with only minimal exposure to UVR. These are found in certain plants and were known to the ancient Egyptians. Unfortunately for the Egyptians it is now known that psoralens can bind to DNA and prevent cell replication, so these compounds are not suitable for everyday use.

As well as the simple protective role of sunscreens there is now exciting evidence that some of these products may even help the body to repair some of the damage produced by the sun. In experiments carried out on hairless mice it was found that repair could occur, even after severe damage, once exposure to UVR was blocked. Broad regions of fresh, young collagen were deposited in the dermis, just below the epidermis, pushing the old structureless material downwards. The new collagen was healthy and normal, and accompanied by a complement of fresh elastin fibres. A similar repair has been observed in biopsies from photodamaged humans who have avoided sun exposure for a number of years. So it seems repair can occur if the skin is not subjected to any more UV light – which means using a sunscreen constantly. This conclusion is emphasised by another experiment in which groups of hairless mice were irradiated for 30 weeks with UVB. Sunscreen was applied to one group after 10 weeks, another after 20 weeks, and a final group was left without protection. The unprotected animals had the severe damage that you would expect, while damage to the other groups reflected the amount of time they had been left unprotected. What was more striking was that in the two protected groups repair zones of new sub-epidermal collagen developed; if a sunscreen is used repair can occur even in the face of continuing UVR irradiation.

Unfortunately this does not mean that someone with a wrinkled face will be able to remove these wrinkles by apply-ing sunscreen. By the time the sun-induced wrinkles occur there has already been severe photodamage, and it is unlikely the body will be able to repair all this damage. Early use of sunscreens will help prevent wrinkles, but damaged faces need more than sunscreen to repair them – and the cosmetics industry is happy to attempt to oblige.

The skin-care business is hitting the headlines. There are more products which are promising to do more than ever before in the areas of anti-ageing and wrinkle control. To succeed in the modern skin-care business you have to have your very own 'regenerator' – the buzzword for a potion that claims to banish facial lines. As the end of the twentieth century approaches, the beauty counters are laden with promises of everlasting youth, and in this billion dollar industry every new product comes weighed down with scientific papers and data to lend it credibility. To understand just what can and cannot be achieved we need to go back to basics.

As we saw earlier, with age the stratum corneum becomes rough and scaly, and starts to feel 'dry'. In profile it is very irregular because as we get older the horny cells clump together to form fish-like scales. In youth, horny cells normally separ-ate into small clusters and are more or less invisibly shed. In dry skin, the cells are shed in the form of these scales. The scales normally cling to the stratum corneum along only one of their edges, and the other edges curl upwards. An object moving over this 'dry surface' catches on these scales – clothing will tend to become entangled with them, for example. In areas where the horny layer is thick, as on the back of the knuckles, it is easy to see that it becomes hard and brittle.

The suppleness of the ageing horny layer depends on the temperature and humidity of the atmosphere. When the atmo-sphere causes the water content of the horny layer to drop, it loses its ability to stretch with the dermis, so that any bodily movement is likely to cause cracks and fissures, particularly on the backs of the hands. These cracks may reach down into the epidermis leading to inflammation and perhaps even bleeding. After the age of about 50 dry skin, especially of the lower legs, becomes ever more common. Because it often itches it interferes with sleep, provokes scratching and is a general nuisance. The critical factor is low relative humidity and particularly a decrease in the absolute moisture content of the air. In the UK these conditions are most likely to occur on cold, dry days in winter. They also occur inside overheated houses and offices. Wind also plays a part; a dry wind will dry out skin very effectively. Dry, hot climates will also lead to dry skin.

In 1952 I. H. Blank published the results of a series of experiments which have since come to be regarded as classic, laying the foundation upon which the concept of the 'moisturiser' is based. Using skin taken from corpses, he demonstrated that dry skin could be softened by water. Even long-term soaking in oils failed to produce a comparable degree of softening. Most scientists now agree that a minimum of 10 per cent water is needed in the stratum corneum in order to produce flexibility and softness. Blank did not suggest that lack of water *caused* 'dry' skin; merely that adding water removed the scaliness and fissures associated with the condition. Fundamentally, 'dry' skin is caused by the subtle changes that occur in the horny layer with age. If the horny layer could keep its youthful structure it would not need to be softened.

Blank's research gave a scientific basis to the concept of the 'moisturiser', a term coined by the cosmetics industry which implies that the product will soften the skin by increasing its moisture content. A good moisturiser will make the skin smoother and less scaly in appearance; it will make it more supple and less prone to cracks and fissures. Hopefully, its benefits will linger even after its use is discontinued.

On the basis of Blank's experiments cosmetic scientists suggested three modes of action by which a moisturising agent could work. First, 'occlusion', where chemicals in the moisturiser form an impermeable barrier over the stratum cornea, trapping moisture in the skin. Secondly, the 'humectant' route, where chemicals with a strong affinity for water bind extra water to the skin. Finally, straightforward 'water delivery', where water is incorporated into the moisturiser so that extra water can be worked into the skin. For the last 30 years these have been the principles that companies have used when designing new moisturisers. They have been used to justify a host of exotic (and often expensive) ingredients.

However, there is now growing doubt about whether traditional moisturisers do work in this way. Despite the importance of moisturising creams to millions of women, proper tests have only just been devised to gauge the efficiency of their pet products, and they show that the old ideas do not stand up to proper scientific investigation. The rationale behind the marketing of all sorts of hi-tech moisturising cocktails has been blown apart. The products almost certainly work, otherwise no one would buy them, but their efficiency as moisturisers probably has more to do with some of the humbler (and cheaper) ingredients.

The problems with the theory of 'occlusion' were first revealed during experiments designed to investigate the outstanding ability of petroleum jelly to remove symptoms of 'dry' skin. Petroleum jelly has always been regarded as the classic 'occlusive' moisturiser: it is a tenacious substance which stays in place, filling in irregularities and smoothing down scales for many hours. However, if its mode of action is occlusion, then its benefits should start disappearing as soon as it is washed off.

This is not the case. A week of treatment greatly reduces scaly skin, and it is another week before the beneficial effects wear off; similarly a two-week treatment wards off dry skin for two weeks after the treatment comes to an end. After three weeks of treatment the scaly skin is obliterated, but more impressively, the skin still shows some suppleness three weeks later.

This has led to speculation that old-fashioned petroleum jelly actually rejuvenates the epidermal production line so that the cells in the stratum corneum behave in a more youthful manner. The stratum corneum is replaced about every three weeks, so if petroleum jelly does affect epidermal production a three-week treatment would give a layer produced entirely during the course of the treatment, and we would expect to find a long-term effect – which is just what happens. A one-week treatment would lead to only one-third of the stratum corneum being formed of 'healthier' cells, and so the beneficial effects would be much diluted and fade away that much sooner. Added evidence that petroleum jelly does penetrate the skin and cause subtle changes is provided by the fact that prolonged use of this cocktail of organic compounds gradually leads to thickening of the epidermis. No one knows why petroleum jelly is so good at alleviating dry skin, but it certainly does not work by occlusion alone.

Lanolin is another traditional 'occlusive' moisturiser which always passes comparative tests with flying colours – although it is not as good a moisturiser as petroleum jelly in that a three-week treatment leads to a relapse in the condition of the skin within two weeks. Once again the persistence of its benefits shows that occlusion alone cannot explain its success as a moisturiser. Furthermore it has now been shown that although lanolin is greasy and sticky, it is actually rather permeable to water, so it cannot work by trapping water in the skin! There is another experiment which also taps a nail into the coffin of the occlusion theory of moisturisers. When you wrap dry skin tightly in plastic film there is no improvement in the condition of the skin, even though every scrap of moisture is being held in.

There are also question marks as to whether water-grabbing humectant chemicals do anything to alleviate the problems of dry skin. It is often the latest exotic humectant that the marketing men use to sell the product, and scientists have exercised enormous ingenuity in dreaming up fresh compounds. Many have their basis in chemicals found in the body.

The stratum corneum contains some very effective natural humectants, which is why it can hold up to six times its own weight in water. These are often described as the natural moisturising factor (NMF), and an enormous amount of work has been done to discover the chemicals which are important in NMF. Opinions differ as to the answer. One candidate is sodium pyrrolidone carboxylic acid (NaPCA), a chemical present in the stratum corneum which can pick up water to the extent of 60 per cent of its own weight. It is now a selling point for a wide range of moisturising creams and is even sold on its own as a 'natural' moisturiser. Other humectants which have come from studying the NMF include urea, various amino acids such as glycine and histidine, and sugars like ribose and deoxyribose. All of them are heavily promoted with lines like 'so powerful it pulls water from the air into your skin'.

Another powerful natural humectant which is currently in vogue is hyaluronic acid, one of the major components of the gel surrounding the collagen and elastin in the dermis, where its incredible affinity for water plays an important part in regulating the overall moisture content of the skin. Its ability to hold water is greater than any other natural or synthetic polymer: a two per cent solution in water holds the remaining 98 per cent of water so tightly that it can be picked up as though it were a gel. Individual molecules of hyaluronic acid bind together to form tangled chains which then mop up water just like a sponge. When it is applied to the surface of the skin it forms a high water content film and helps boost the water content of the stratum corneum. For the cosmetic companies it has the added advantage that this film is not greasy or tacky. It is so ubiquitous in the body that the immune system does not react to it, and so it is able to play a vital role in lubricating and protecting sensitive tissue in eye operations, and in the treatment of arthritis, where injections help to protect and lubricate painful joints.

There are also more old-fashioned humectants such as propylene glycol, glycerol and sorbitol. Propylene glycol is used in many facial products because it rubs in more easily than glycerol, which is more common in hand moisturisers. However there is enormous controversy among dermatologists as to whether these substances (which undoubtedly do have an affinity for water) do anything at all to help cure 'dry' skin.

Despite the sales pitches, application of these humectants on their own is of little use. It is true that when they are applied to pieces of skin in the laboratory they increase the water content of the horny layer, which does lead to increased suppleness and softness. However they are unlikely to be able to achieve this in everyday life because they are all highly water soluble and so are easily dissolved away by sweat or any moisture in the air.

Effective cosmetics have to be able to stay on the skin.

As a result most humectants are incorporated into a basic moisturising mix. When tests were recently carried out on a range of moisturising creams to measure how much the humectants improved the quality of the moisturiser, it was found that they made little difference. These tests involved manufacturing various moisturising creams with and without their humectants and then using them to treat people with dry skin. It was found that the added humectants made no noticeable difference, an observation that held both for humble chemicals like propylene glycol, glycerol and sorbitol, and for their more expensive equivalents like NaPCA and urea. The humectants probably do add water to the horny layer, but this seems to be a minor, unobservable contribution to the success of the moisturiser.

Finally, even though virtually all moisturising creams are emulsions which contain water as a major (and sometimes expensive) product, moisturisers cannot completely owe their success to their ability to deliver water to the skin, since any water in the emulsion will evaporate rapidly as soon as the emulsion is rubbed into the skin.

Many researchers now think that many so-called 'moisturising' creams work simply by sticking down loosened flakes, altering the way that light is reflected from the skin's surface, and making it appear more transparent and youthful. The greasiness of the moisturiser also helps bind the layer together so that it does not crack or fissure, and cuts down friction so that the skin feels smoother.

The effect of water alone is minuscule compared to the overall covering and lubricating effects of the greasy products found in moisturisers. To this extent all greasy substances are to some extent moisturisers, which explains why different moisturisers are able to use widely differing chemicals as their base. Most of these products offer no long-term benefits because they do not alter the basic ageing process of the horny layer, but instead hide its effects – something which they often do very effectively.

The cosmetic scientists have now gone back to basics to try to discover compounds which can have a long-term effect in combating the ageing horny layer. To do this an enormous amount of work has been put into understanding the chemistry responsible for the layer's ability to act as a barrier to water and other chemicals. It has become clear that this is a much more subtle process than was ever suspected. For example, deficiencies of essential fatty acids lead to much higher rates of water loss from the skin, and dryness and scaliness. The first clue to this came when dermatologists discovered that applications of linoleic acid will remedy some dry skin conditions. (Linoleic acid is now included in some moisturisers: however this presupposes that the people buying the cream have dry skin caused by a fatty acid deficiency).

It looks likely that a better understanding of the biochemistry of the stratum corneum is going to lead to a new generation of hi-tech moisturisers whose success will have nothing at all to do with greasiness. Some of the most recent work suggests that fatty chemicals known as lipids, found in the spaces between cells in the stratum corneum, may be far more important than was ever suspected. It has always been assumed that these lipids help to form a physical barrier to water loss, but it now seems they also control the chemicals responsible for freeing cells from the stratum corneum so that they can be sloughed off. These lipids are very rich in linoleic acid, which explains why a deficiency of this chemical will lead to 'dry' skin: cell shedding will start to slow down and the cells in the horny layer will start to clump into scales. It seems that alpha-hydroxy acids like lactic acid owe their mysterious moisturising effects to some subtle chemical effect on the lipids in the epidermis which causes an increased loss of cells and so a reduction in scaliness.

The presence of lipids in the stratum corneum is being exploited by a new variation on the old moisturiser theme. Traditional moisturising agents such as NaPCA are trapped inside substances called liposomes which bind to the lipids with the result that the moisturising agent is held in the stratum corneum and not quickly washed off by sweat or moisture. There is no doubt that liposome-based compounds are among the more effective – and less greasy – moisturising creams. However, despite their cost and sophistication, they are still no more effective than that old stalwart, petroleum jelly. The hunt is still on for chemicals which display more dramatic effects.

Unfortunately, even if some revolutionary products are found to put an end to dry, scaly skin, it is most unlikely that they will be able to do anything to hide the wrinkles and lines which appear on the ageing face. As we have seen, these arise from changes in the epidermis and the dermis, not in the stratum corneum. However, more and more 'anti-ageing' products are now coming on to the market which claim to be able to restore the epidermis and dermis to their youthful state.

Anti-wrinkle compounds first began to take a significant share of the skin care market in the mid-1960s, a time when most of them were based on bovine serum albumen. This substance was hailed in the press releases as 'an amazing new cosmetic that temporarily erases facial wrinkles and lines, smoothing skin to a fresh young texture within a matter of minutes, and keeping the wrinkles and lines away for hours'. It was claimed that its revitalising action would last up to eight hours or longer after a week to ten days' regular use.

Bovine serum albumen is obtained from cows' blood by first removing the blood cells, distilling out the plasma, and finally drying the serum. When a solution of the substance was applied to the face it dried to a film which, as it contracted, lifted the underlying wrinkles up to the same level as the surrounding skin. It normally showed an effect within about five minutes which could then last anywhere between two and six hours. Examinations of treated skin under a steroscope showed that fine wrinkles gradually became invisible, while deeper wrinkles became shallower. However, unless very large amounts were used, the contracting film was not strong enough to lift out lines on the forehead, and around the eyes and mouth.

Bovine serum albumen has now fallen out of favour. It would start to flake off if you laughed or smiled too much, and so you had to choose between beauty and smiles. Just as importantly, its mode of action is rather too straightforward for the marketing men to be able to sell in the present hi-tech cosmetic industry.

In the past a great deal of effort has gone into producing hormone-based anti-wrinkle creams. Back in 1937 a chance discovery in a pharmaceutical plant led to the development of a wide range of oestrogen-containing cosmetics. Women filling ampoules with oil-suspended oestrogens for intra-muscular injections noticed that after a few months on the production line the skin on the back of their hands began to lose its wrinkles. Cosmetic scientists rushed to exploit this discovery, and in the late 1930s the first oestrogen-containing cosmetic, Endocrene, hit the market. There were soon many others.

Sadly, it was to no avail: hormone creams have now gone out of fashion. Oestrogen is a potent chemical, and it is known that in high levels it can lead to cancer. As a result only very tiny amounts can be used in any cosmetic preparation. Because the levels are so low the creams do not produce the cut and dried results that the women on the production line noticed, and many scientists believe that, quite simply, the levels of hormones that have to be used in cosmetics are too low to achieve anything.

Most cosmetic companies view hormones with suspicion. They are so potent they could easily produce horrific side effects and crippling law suits. Nevertheless, research is continuing, and although the mechanism by which oestrogen removes wrinkles is not fully understood, it does seem that it is able to stimulate the skin into producing fresh cells. Hormones are unlikely to appear on the cosmetic stands until chemical delivery systems capable of transporting minute doses to specific tissues in the skin are developed. That way small doses can still be highly active – and the hormone will not go further into the body. With selective-site hormone delivery, cosmetic scientists would be able to formulate mixtures to stimulate collagen and elastin production, or fat removal, or even hair production. As we shall see later, such chemical delivery systems are under development; if they are successful cosmetic science could be revolutionised.

The guiding principles used by cosmetic scientists in devising today's anti-ageing compounds are deceptively simple. The changes in the epidermis are caused by a slower rate of cell manufacture which comes with increasing age. The scientists are therefore hunting to find methods of stimulating cell production. In the dermis most of the problems are caused by damaged connective tissue, and so the search is on for materials which will slow down this damage and stimulate ageing fibroblast cells which produce fresh connective tissue. It would also be useful to be able to plump up the water content of the epidermis and the dermis so that the ground substance, the gel between the connective tissue, could more easily fill out wrinkles and lines.

It sounds simple, but there are some immense complications. Even if chemicals are isolated which can achieve these goals, the formulators are still left with the tricky problem of delivering them into the epidermis and the dermis – and since one of the main purposes of the skin is to keep out strange chemicals, sneaking cosmetic potions past the stratum corneum is no easy matter. Even if the cosmetic scientists find an answer to this conundrum, they still have to grapple with cells in the skin like the Langerhans cells whose whole purpose is to destroy foreign chemicals which manage to pass through the horny layer. Despite these difficulties, the cosmetics industry has come up with plenty of suggestions to rejuvenate the skin.

Scrubbing off the surface of the skin is the simplest notion – a method which after all the acres of advertising extolling silky, smoothing creams sounds like heresy of the highest order. The logic is that the production of epidermal cells must, over a period of time, balance the rate at which cells are shed, and so scrubbing off cells must stimulate the epidermis into manufacturing replacements. A young skin renews its surface layer every two to three weeks, while a mature skin may take double that time, and so the hope is that scrubbing will force the epidermis into a frenzy of youthful reproduction. A more youthful epidermis should mean less scaliness and none of the irregularities which lead to wrinkling. Whether this is the case remains a matter of controversy: abrasion certainly leads to less scaliness, but its effect on wrinkles is still disputed. In the meantime a wide range of 'facial scrubs' have stormed on to the skin care market and taken a substantial slice of the action.

As we have already seen, alpha-hydroxy acids like lactic acid also increase the rate at which cells are shed, and indeed so do a number of mild skin irritants: these are now commonly added to many moisturisers at such low concentrations that their irritant action is not noticeable enough to be painful.

Neither of these techniques require any chemicals to be able to pass through the stratum corneum. However more and more anti-ageing therapies claim to carry the fight against the ageing process deep into the dermis and the epidermis.

The greatest excitement in the cosmetics world currently centres around retinoic acid (vitamin A) and its derivatives – often referred to as 'retinoids'. We saw earlier that skin protected from sunlight can start to repair itself, and the cosmetics industry has been hunting for chemicals that are able to stimulate this rather slow natural repair system. This is where retinoic acid and the retinoids come in. Although retinoids are known to inhibit the growth of many cells in the laboratory, they actually stimulate the growth of fibroblasts, the cells which produce new growth in the dermis and epidermis. This, together with reports that these compounds accelerate wound repair, has led to experiments at the University of Pennsylvania to test a particular form of retinoic acid known as all-trans retinoic acid (RA) as a repair enhancer.

Hairless mice were irradiated with UVB for 10 weeks so that their connective tissue was mildly damaged. These mice were then divided into three groups. One group had RA rubbed into their skins three times a day for five weeks, another for 10 weeks. The final group was left untreated. The results indicated that RA does help to repair damage: there were large areas of rejuvenated dermis in the treated animals, particularly in those treated for 10 weeks. As well as this fresh collagen and elastin, the number of fibroblasts had increased and they were in a frenzy of activity.

These are results which are still puzzling scientists, because retinoids usually have little effect on collagen synthesis when fibroblasts are nurtured in the laboratory, and indeed they sometimes cut down the rate of collagen production. However in studies with living animals it does seem the reverse happens. We may not know how they work, but retinoids are already finding their way into some of the anti-ageing products sold over the beauty counters.

Retinoic acid is unusual in that it is one of the chemicals that can pass through the barrier posed by the horny layer. But anti-ageing therapies claim to be able to infiltrate a wide variety of other chemicals past the stratum corneum because of developments in liposome technology. We have already encountered liposomes as vehicles for carrying moisture into the stratum corneum. In fact the world of medicine uses them for far more sophisticated tasks, and the cosmetics industry believes that these techniques can be applied in the battle against ageing.

The liposome is a chemical container synthesised to resemble a cell membrane. When used to carry drugs it can either be a straightforward envelope, or a set of concentric spheres with the drug trapped between each layer. The immune system does not attack liposomes in the same way that other chemicals would be attacked because of their resemblance to the body's cells, and so liposomes can travel around the body for some time. Eventually the immune system realises that the liposomes are foreign and breaks them down. This often means that the transported drug is released into the liver and spleen, and so liposomes already play an important role in treating liver diseases. The hope for the future is that chemical markers can be attached to the outside of the liposomes so that they will be able to home in on specific areas of the body – including, perhaps, the skin. This lies in the future, but cosmetic companies still make wide use of liposomes and other related chemicals because they claim that they can penetrate the stratum corneum, and deliver a host of active ingredients to the epidermis and the dermis. As with so many claims in this industry, there are violent arguments about the truth of this one.

Whether or not they are loaded into transport chemicals like liposomes, free radical scavengers and anti-oxidants are present in most anti-ageing lotions. We have seen that free radicals wreak havoc in the dermis when they break through the body's defences, and so most anti-ageing products contain a selection of scavengers and anti-oxidants designed to mop them up. Vitamin E (alpha tocopherol), vitamin C (ascorbic acid) and beta carotene all fall into this category. The two vitamins also offer additional benefits. Vitamin E can be combined with nicotinic acid to produce a compound that can mop up free radicals, and cause the blood vessels in the skin to dilate, increasing the flow of nutrients to the area, and adding colour to the skin. Vitamin C is also thought to play an important role in the chemical processes which produce fresh connective tissue.

As we saw in Chapter Three, there is no doubt about the important role that these substances play in suppressing the damage that can be caused by free radicals, but there is great doubt about whether applying them to the skin is of any use. The dose delivered in a cosmetic is tiny compared to the quantities that can be delivered by just eating these vitamins, and it would be overwhelmed by the first mouthful of cigarette smoke.

Just to complicate matters, in the normal course of events the body decides the quantities of these chemicals it is going to manufacture for the skin. When it senses the cosmetically applied vitamins, it may close down its own production, and the net result will be that the skin will receive no extra quota of free radical scavengers. There is evidence that this is what happens in the case of vitamin E.

Other chemicals loaded into liposomes by cosmetic companies are collagen and elastin peptides, the building blocks from which these connective fibres are constructed. Again there is great controversy over whether these chemicals do anything to help build fresh collagen and elastin in the dermis. As the experiments with retinoic acid indicate, the body is able to manufacture fresh collagen and elastin when it wishes to. The problem is getting it to turn on the manufacturing process. Simply delivering the building blocks for repair could be like dumping a lorry load of bricks on a building site and then expecting them to self-assemble. Until conclusive evidence is produced that these peptides lead to increased repair rates, the rationale for using them is weak.

Many companies include various chemical forms of collagen in their products – indeed at one time collagen was the magic ingredient upon which many creams were based. If your own is wilting, stiffen it up, ran the thinking. A few simple experiments with radioactively labelled collagen soon showed this to be a ridiculous argument. No radioactivity from the collagen applied to the skin was ever detected under the stratum corneum. This is hardly surprising because a back of an envelope calculation easily shows that collagen molecules (especially those taken from calves, the usual source) are far too large to penetrate through the stratum corneum. However some collagen products are still included in moisturising creams because they form a film on the surface of the skin, making it feel smooth, and helping to protect the skin from attack by detergents (which is why many shampoos contain a dose of these particular products).

Substances called tropocollagens are also included in many of the latest anti-ageing remedies. Tropocollagen molecules are the molecules initially produced by the fibroblasts which then go on to organise themselves into a full collagen molecule. The justification for using tropocollagens is that when they are applied to wounds, healing is accelerated. Unfortunately, this does not mean that they will accelerate skin repair when used in cosmetics. The concentrations used in medicine are enormously high, and anyway, there is no evidence that they can penetrate the skin (a part of the process that is unnecessary when you are applying these substances to an open wound).

Other popular additives are substances like hyaluronic acid, the chemical which, as we have already seen, is responsible for storing much of the water in the dermis and epidermis. It is likely that the amount of hyaluronic acid decreases with age and so boosting the level should increase the skin's plumpness and puff out wrinkles. However it is the enormous size of hyaluronic acid molecules which allows them to trap water molecules in a vast polymeric structure; this size means that they are far too large to travel through the stratum corneum, and far too large to be contained within a liposome. Hyaluronic acid cannot, with present technology, be transported to the epidermis or dermis. Whereas conventional moisturisers merely slick down the outer surface, the new anti-ageing products all claim to penetrate deep into the epidermis where cell renewal takes place. A few claim to reach the dermis itself, with the chance of entering the bloodstream.

The arrival in 1986 of a controversial treatment called Glycel heightened public awareness of such developments. Glycel's vital ingredients, GSL or glycosphospholipids, were brand new and were promoted by a man with a unique medical pedigree. Former heart transplant pioneer, Christiaan

Barnard, endorsed the action of GSLs by claiming that 'a lot of the ageing changes you see in the skin are due to environmental damage, so if you have an agent in a skin care product that will promote the healing of cells damaged by environmental factors surely it will be of value'. The claims for products based on GSLs have embroiled the cosmetics industry in a controversy which may ultimately change the working practices of the whole industry. As far as Glycel was concerned the resulting furore affected sales and it was soon withdrawn from many leading stores.

It has been known for some years that GSLs are found in all animal cells and many plant cells, but until recently no one paid them much attention because it was not clear what their function was. Indeed their mouthful of a name reflected the mystery that surrounded them. The first glycosphosphingolipid was discovered in brain tissue in 1874 by Johann Ludwig Thudichum. He called the particular compound he had discovered 'cerebroside', but gave the class of chemicals the romantic prefix 'sphingo'. In Greek mythology the fearsome monster Sphinx, part woman and part winged lion, terrorised the city of Thebes by devouring all who could not correctly answer her riddles. For many years the riddle of GSLs would continue. Over the last decade, however, cancer immunologists have subjected GSLs to intense scrutiny. It is now known that they are studded into the membranes of every cell in the body, and that they play vital roles in determining how we develop and grow.

Animal cells can normally only divide to produce another cell when triggered to do so by the arrival of growth hormones in the fluid surrounding the cell. The growth hormones bind to special receptor sites on the surface of cells, and precipitate a chain of chemical events which eventually causes the cell to divide. However the presence of certain GSLs in the membrane can prevent division because they interact with the receptor sites to prevent the growth hormones from triggering cell division. The GSL environment of the membrane determines whether or not the cell will divide and reproduce. Furthermore a complex chain of chemical events allows GSLs to determine how many similar cells are close by, and this affects whether they allow cell division or not.

GSLs have another vital function. They serve as 'markers' which identify the cells as 'self' so that the immune system never attacks healthy cells. They are the body's 'Friend or Foe' device. So, for example, it is GSLs which mark your blood cells and decide which blood group you belong to. GSLs also mark in such a way that the body can tell whether a cell is a blood cell, a liver cell, or a brain cell.

It is clear that any disruption in the way that GSLs work in the body could cause chaotic, undisciplined growth, as well as a breakdown in the immune system. This is exactly what happens in cancer. It is now clear that cancerous growth is intimately associated with altered GSLs. Many cancer cells, for example, manufacture novel forms of GSLs, or accumulate simple forms because the synthesis of the more complex GSLs is somehow blocked.

It is strange, then, to find such potent chemicals being included in a cosmetic lotion whose aim is to stimulate fresh growth in the dermis. The world's top cancer experts openly admit that the way in which GSLs interact with the rest of the body's system is nowhere near understood – if it was we might have a much better understanding of cancer. It therefore seems unlikely that anyone can be sure about what effect they may have in a cosmetic – especially as at the time of writing there are no published papers in major scientific journals on how skin care products containing GSLs are meant to work.

The main cause of Glycel's decline lies in the city of Washington DC where early in 1986 the Federal Drug Administration started to cast a jaundiced eye at the anti-ageing business. Regulatory letters were sent out to 23 firms accusing them of making drug claims. According to the FDA, the cosmetics industry did not heed the FDA's advice to regulate itself. The FDA has constantly urged the industry that if they wanted to make anti-ageing claims for their products then they had to be considered as drugs, which would require new drug applications being filed before the product was marketed. It was emphasised that they should not make claims to boost the sales of their products without being able to prove them scientifically.

The use of such potent chemicals has raised the heckles of the FDA. In this particular case most scientists think that little harm can be done because it is widely reckoned that the GSL molecules are far too large to pass through the stratum corneum (although Dr Barnard insists the opposite is true). However, the FDA have taken the position that if the GSLs do not penetrate into the dermis then the consumer is being tricked, while if they do, a potent drug is being sold without proper clinical tests.

Alfin have now said that it is not economically feasible for them to comply with the FDA's demands, and the product, at the time of writing, is being withdrawn. Predictions of sales worth hundreds of millions by 1990 have come to nothing.

Although all cosmetics must be subjected to exhaustive checks to make sure there are no toxic side effects, the Glycel furore may force the companies to undertake full clinical trials on all their products. Even for the big name cosmetic houses this is a terrifying prospect, not only because of the huge sums of money involved but also because the time these trials would take would mean the companies would be unable to react to the latest cosmetic fashions. Even those firms which have offered to adjust their advertising claims have so far failed to satisfy the FDA.

It is highly unlikely that cosmetic companies in the UK will suffer from the same problems. In the UK the cosmetics industry is controlled by consumer protection legislation whose definition of a cosmetic is much more straightforward: 'any product or preparation intended to be applied to any part of the exterior surfaces of the human body, wholly or mainly for the purposes of cleansing or protecting or keeping them in good condition'. As far as this definition is concerned, nothing can be a drug which is not designed to treat or prevent disease. Since ageing is considered to be a natural process and not a disease, there are only two ways that any cosmetic could fail to come up to the mark; there could be complaints to the local authority Trading Standards department which could lead to a prosecution in the magistrates' court, or the official watchdog of the advertising industry, the Advertising Standards Authority, could investigate whether anti-ageing claims are legal, decent, honest and truthful. However, some members of the Committee for the Safety of Medicines believe that legislation may be required to force anti-ageing compounds to be treated as drugs.

There is – on the horizon – a further threat to the cosmetics industry's domination of the skin-care market. A research team in Denmark sponsored by a British biotechnology company have thrown up what could be the first unashamedly medical solution to the problem of ageing skin. The team, led by Professor Brian Clark at the University of Aarhus, claim to have discovered a 'natural' compound which, under laboratory conditions, can delay ageing in skin cells and, still more remarkably, reverse the ageing process in skin cells that have already deteriorated because of age. The nature and origins of the compound, so far simply called Factor X, are being kept secret; the researchers will say only that it is an extract of a natural material – not skin – which they stumbled across by chance. The researchers say that Factor X works not by causing cells to live longer, but by somehow altering the biochemistry of ageing cells so that they return to a more youthful state. Like Dorian Grey, the cells will continue to age, but without showing it. They will die in the same way as they would have anyway, but functioning until the last moment like young cells. Brian Clark and his team hope that by incorporating Factor X into a skin cream they will be able to banish wrinkles for ever.

What distinguishes Factor X from other elixirs of youth is that its inventors are currently preparing to put it though full and stringent clinical trials. This is partly because the company involved hopes that the product will also find widespread use as a drug to hasten the healing of burns. The trials will provide definitive proof of whether Factor X, which so far has only been tested on skin cells in laboratory cultures, can rejuvenate skin cells still functioning as part of the human body.

It could be that Factor X, for whatever reason, never makes it on to the market. But it is a sign of the times that medical researchers are now moving into the skin care business. If the cosmetics industry is faced with a fully tried and tested drug, accepted by the medical authorities as capable of rejuvenating skin, the age of the cosmeceutical will begin in earnest.

While women peer into the mirror looking for wrinkles, lines, sagging features and grey hairs, men tend to have just one thing on their minds: baldness. They may try to pretend otherwise, but the evidence is against them. In 1983, a hospital in Washington DC took the foolish step of announcing that it was looking for volunteers to test a new anti-baldness potion. Later the same day the harassed doctor in charge of the tests found himself explaining to reporters why the hospital had ground to a halt: 'We immediately got ten thousand calls from across the country. The calls overwhelmed the hospital's trunk lines and froze the switchboard. We had to gear up our disaster control centre and staff the phones with volunteers from the accounting department.'

For naked apes we all worry a great deal about the small amount of hair that we have got. The hair-care industry persuaded people in Britain to part with 126 million pounds last year for shampoo alone. In the US sales of hair preparations have grown at an annual rate of 10 per cent for the last eight years. In 1987 it is estimated that Americans will spend about five billion dollars to clean, condition, curl, straighten, colour, mousse and gel their locks, more than the 1987 budget request for the Star Wars programme.

The reason that we have far less hair than apes is not because we have fewer hair follicles than, say, chimpanzees, but because most of our follicles produce fine, short hair rather than long fur. The exception, of course, is the head. In a normal head of hair there are somewhere between 100,000 and 120,000 hairs – more in blondes, less in redheads.

In essence a hair is a long thin fibre composed mainly of proteins called keratins. All skin is keratinized, and hair, nails, horns and hooves are all just local thickenings of keratin. In fact, just like fingernails, hairs are dead; they are not composed of living cells, and they do not need any nutrition.

Hairs are produced in pits in the skin known as follicles – when we talk about hair roots we are in fact talking about follicles. Each of us has around two million follicles scattered over our body. Inside the follicle the hair shaft is created, pigmented, assembled, oiled by the sebaceous glands, sent out to battle with the elements and finally discarded.

Seen under a microscope, each hair is covered with tiny overlapping scales, forming a layer called the cuticle which encloses the cortex of the hair shaft. The function of the cuticle is to protect this shaft, and it does this in many ways. There is a cement that holds overlapping scales together, and when a hair is cut this cement oozes out to seal the end of the hair against the elements. Within each cell is a layer of keratin that protects the shaft from mechanical and chemical damage. Aside from the cement, cuticle cells are also joined by so-called 'press studs', jigsaw-like protuberances which lock into each other and 'rivets', protein-like strands that appear to cross the membranes of adjacent cells and hold them together. The cuticle thus forms a formidable barrier around the hair, keeping it in good condition.

The cortex is a tangle of five-ply keratin cables embedded in a protein matrix. These threads twist together in groups of five to form a yarn of what are known as microfibrils. This yarn is in turn bundled into cables, and twisting and tangling of microfibrils between different cables means that each hair shaft is tough and elastic. Provided that our hair did not fall out from its roots, most of us could quite safely suspend ourselves from just one thousand of the tens of thousands of hairs that make up a healthy head of hair.

Each hair starts to grow in the base of the follicle, where a system of tiny blood vessels supply an area of rapidly dividing cells with nutrients. As these cells move upwards and away from this zone of multiplication they become increasingly keratinized, drying, hardening and ultimately dying in the process. As the hair emerges from the follicle it passes through a narrow funnel that acts rather like a rolling mill, sealing the cuticle cells on the outside of the hair.

The keratin that makes up a hair shaft is colourless – just as fingernails are. The colour of our hair is determined by highly specialised cells called melanocytes. These exist at the base of the follicle and secrete tiny granules of pigment into the spaces in the keratin. The colour of our hair depends upon how many of these granules are trapped in the hair shaft. Deep black Bantu hair contains many granules, and these are present in the cuticle as well as the inner hair shaft. Black Japanese hair has just as many granules in the hair shaft, but fewer in the cuticle. Even the darkest European hair contains very few granules in the cuticle. Granules from light blonde European hair consist of a very little melanin embedded in a colourless ground. Very dark hair, apart from having a lot of granules, also has a lot of melanin in each granule.

The scalp has some 100,000 follicles, or some 1,000 per square inch. Blondes can have up to 140,000, but they tend to produce thinner hair than their more pigmented counterparts. Brunettes have 110,000 follicles, redheads 90,000. During a person's lifetime the scalp follicles produce more than fifteen pounds of hair. Thin hairs come out of skinny follicles, while coarse ones come out of large ones. The mightiest follicles are those which produce beards, whilst the most diminutive are the follicles which produce the tiniest hairs of all, those on the nose and the tops of the ears and eyelids.

Each of the hair follicles follows its own programme, regardless of what the follicles around it are doing. The anagenic or growing phase is when the hair is being formed. In women it lasts around six years during which time the hair – if it is allowed to – will grow to between 70 and 80 centimetres. In men the anagenic phase is only four years and so the maximum length is correspondingly shorter – about 40 centimetres.

The next phase is the telegenic or resting phase. The root end of the hair becomes clubbed and anchors itself to the follicle with fibrous rootlets. The follicle itself shrivels.

On a non-balding scalp, some time between three and six months later the follicle reactivates and starts to grow a new hair. If the old one has not already fallen out, it will be pushed out by this new growth. About one hundred of these mature hairs are shed each day as normal turnover. Luckily the follicles are all in different phases at different times, otherwise everyone would have several months of balding every four or five years. At any given time 85 per cent of our follicles are growing hair, while around 15 per cent are resting.

There are many people who find that as they become older their hair loses its sheen and becomes dry and brittle. In fact, this has nothing to do with any fundamental process of ageing, and everything to do with the habits they have slipped into over the years when looking after their hair. After all, hair is replaced every four to six years, and there is no reason why it should deteriorate with age.

A glance at the microscopic appearance of hair in bad

condition reveals a disaster in the cuticular layer. Instead of a closer-packed sheath of interlocking cells, the edges of the cells have lifted off, exposing the hair shaft below. This damage allows moisture to escape from the cortex, making the hair dry and brittle. It also impairs the reflectivity of hair, so that it looks dull. To add to this tale of woe the raised scales catch each other, tangling the hair.

Damage to the cuticle can be caused by a range of factors. When you comb or brush your hair the force you exert at the root of the hair is quite low, but as you whip down the hair, the force exerted becomes progressively greater, and cuticle cells at the tip of the hair start to be displaced or eroded. The more vigorous the combing and brushing, the more damage. If the damage is so great that the cuticle layer is completely removed, the keratin fibres in the cortex are exposed to the open air and start to unwind, and you become the owner of a 'split end'.

Combing or brushing wet hair does even more damage because the frictional forces between wet hairs are far greater than between dry hairs, and correspondingly greater muscle power is exerted to force the comb or brush through the hair. In fact even rubbing wet hair with a towel can cause a great deal of damage, because when hair is rubbed against the direction the cuticles lie in, they are likely to be raised and even pulled off.

Once hair is damaged it cannot be repaired. What you can do is make it look better, and make it easier to comb so that you won't inflict similar damage on any new hair. This is what hair conditioners do. All conditioners aim to smooth down the surface of individual hairs. If they can achieve this a number of other benefits will then occur. The latest conditioners rely on silicones. Even in tiny quantities they form a protective film around the hair and prevent further damage by reducing the friction between the hair and the brush. This lubrication also stops static electricity from building up during combing, which leads to the 'fly-away look'.

There are further benefits. When the silicone attaches itself to the hair shaft it displaces the moisture on the surface, and so the hair dries more quickly. This provides additional protection against the worst excesses of blow drying. The silicone layer itself provides some sheen and by helping to stick down the raised cuticular cells it improves the shine of the hair even more.

Proteins, usually in the form of hydrolysed animal collagen, are sometimes added to the conditioner to feed the damaged hair. However, since the hair is dead there is nothing to feed. The effects of adding proteins are minimal, although because they are greasy they may help to temporarily coat the damaged hair with a protective layer.

With proper care there is no reason why the quality of your hair should deteriorate with age – provided, of course, that you can keep your hair. The battle men have fought against androgenic alopecia – common male pattern baldness – goes back as far as recorded history. In about 1550 BC a document was written, and later found in the tomb of an Egyptian mummy, that provided a prescription for baldness. The Ebers papyrus called for taking equal parts of fat from a lion, a hippopotamus, a crocodile, a goose, a snake and a goat, mixing and applying liberally to the bald scalp. Roman coins show that Caesar parted his hair over one ear, and draped strands over to the other. Between then and now quacksters have sold men everything from bull semen to mayonnaise to rub into their balding domes. Current favourites are products which claim to supply 'missing' vitamins which promote hair growth and lotions which claim to remove the excess sebum which 'blocks' hair growth. (It doesn't and they don't.) No matter how often men are told that baldness is part of the natural course of life, it is a part that most of them would happily do without.

Until recently the only treatment that has worked has been to take drugs to boost the female hormone levels in the body – and that produces side effects like enlarged breasts and atrophying gonads. There is another way to boost female hormone levels in the body. Most dermatologists like to tell the apocryphal story of the youth with a rapidly receding hairline who pleaded with his doctor to help him stave off baldness. 'There's only one thing we can do to help you,' the doctor pronounced. 'Castration. We'd have to cut off your testicles.' The young man thought for a moment. 'Can you do it now?' he asked.

During the earlier years of life, hair growth holds fairly

constant. However from about 16 to 46 years of age the amount of hair on the scalp decreases progressively in both men and women. This is not because hairs start to fall out, but because more and more follicles move into the telegen, or resting, phase, particularly in the central areas of the scalp. After the age of 50 the amount of hair decreases significantly in both sexes, even in adults with no obvious signs of balding. In this age group the individual hairs tend to be thicker and an even higher proportion of follicles move into the telegen phase.

This long-term loss of hair comes to everyone with increasing age. However, many men and women also start to show signs of what is known as pattern baldness at even earlier ages. Female pattern baldness is fairly restricted, and is characterised by a general thinness of hair throughout the scalp. The most prevalent type of baldness is male pattern baldness (androgenetic alopecia). This typically manifests itself as an 'M'-shaped outline on a receding hairline. Concurrently a balding patch appears on the crown and increases in size, eventually meeting the receding hairline. In its final stage, the total scalp is exposed. The physiology is the same as for long-term hair loss. Not only does the resting stage, telegen, of the hair follicle cycle become progressively longer, but the follicles themselves gradually shrink during the balding process. The change occurs over several successive generations of hair cycles. At each cycle the size of the follicle at the growth stage, anagen, becomes smaller. With each diminution, the hair generated by the follicle becomes shorter, thinner and less pigmented. The process continues until the size of the follicle reaches that of the vellus state in which the hair produced is a minute, colourless filament almost invisible to the eye. It is estimated that nine out of ten men in Britain who experience balding have male pattern baldness. Overall some 7.9 million men suffer from some degree of hair loss.

The percentage of bald men runs just about parallel with age: 25 per cent of 25-year-olds, 50 per cent of 50-year-olds, 75 per cent of 70-year-olds. To be a candidate for baldness a man simply has to have a genetic predisposition towards it (which is possible if anyone in his family on either side, has ever been bald) and have a normal complement of male sex hormones. If you are genetically disposed to balding it is essentially a secondary male sexual characteristic, like the deepening of the voice at puberty.

At puberty the gonads and adrenals secrete androgens – male hormones, the most powerful and prevalent of which is testosterone – into the bloodstream. The liver produces blood plasma proteins that bind to most androgens, leaving only a small percentage of free androgens wandering around in the bloodstream. Some of these enter the cells of the hair follicles, where a specific enzyme, 5-alpha-reductase, converts them into more active androgens called dihydrotestosterone (DHT). This DHT hooks itself on to a highly specific cell protein, and together they move into the nuclei of hair follicle cells, where they stimulate the genetic transmitters that give the follicles their orders. These include commands to the sebaceous glands to step up their oil-producing activity, which contributes to the occurrence of acne. The genetic transmitters also order other follicles in the body – particularly those in the armpits, across the chest, on the face, and in the pubic area – to crank out darker, thicker, longer hair.

Finally, for reasons that are not fully understood, DHT tells the genetic machinery inside some of the scalp molecules to start shutting down. With this, at whatever rate is assigned to them, the follicles begin to atrophy and enter the spiral of decline which we have already seen. It does seem that sebaceous glands in bald scalps have a stronger affinity and a greater capacity for binding male hormones, which may explain in part why certain men are more prone to baldness.

In 1979 the American Federal Drug Administration gave the drug company Upjohn permission to market Loniten tablets as a remedy for high blood pressure. The tablets contained the compound minoxidil, a potent vasodilator (a substance that expands the blood vessels and so lowers blood pressure). Its occasional side effects – dizziness, pain, nausea, increased heart rate, and difficulty in breathing – made it something of a last resort treatment. There was also another side effect. Inexplicably, some people taking the drug found they were growing hair not only on their heads but also randomly over much of their bodies.

Within three to six weeks of starting a course of the drug, longer and darker hair can start to develop. Then comes abnormal hair growth, normally on the temples, between the hairline and the eyebrows, and in the sideburn area. Continued use of minoxidil can then go on to produce significant extra hair growth on the back, legs, arms and scalp.

As word got around of this side effect, minoxidil became a black-market hair restorer, but a highly dangerous one because of its powerful effects on the heart and the blood system. By now the Upjohn scientists had realised that minoxidil was never going to be the world's first choice as a blood pressure tablet. But they did start to wonder what would happen if a safe dose of the drug was dissolved in a lotion and rubbed into a balding scalp.

They named this new product Regaine and in 1982 set out to test it. Over the next two years some 2,300 bald scalps had the potion applied. Upjohn found that one-third of the patients grew an acceptable head of hair, one-third had fuzzy baby hair, and one-third grew no hair at all. For the first time a baldness potion had been found that had some degree of success. When Upjohn announced the results of the test the value of their shares doubled.

Investigators are still not certain how minoxidil produces hair growth. Some scientists attribute its success to its ability to stimulate the blood supply to the scalp, but then there are plenty of other vasodilators which can do this, but do not cause hair growth. Interest is now centering on laboratory experiments which have shown that minoxidil cells called T-cell helpers are vital to the functioning of the immune system. These cells play an important role in controlling the population of the immune system's T cells, the cells responsible for fighting off attacks by bacteria and viruses, and for reacting against transplanted tissue. Added weight is given to this observation by minoxidil's ability to treat alopecia areata, an especially distressing form of baldness where plugs of hair are suddenly lost, exposing patches of the scalp. It is a condition which affects all ages and both sexes, and is caused by a so-called auto-immune reaction, a misdirected immune response which attacks and destroys hair follicles. Two British dermatologists, David Fenton and John Wilkinson, recently found that minoxidil made new hair grow in all their alopecia areata patients. Vellus hair, the fluff found on new-born babies, formed first, and then developed into adult-type hair. It seems that it may be the action of minoxidil on the immune system that will explain its properties.

There are drawbacks. Researchers are still trying to discover how much of the lotion finds its way into the bloodstream. And all the indications are that hair grown with the aid of the drug falls out as soon as the treatment stops. Everyone agrees that minoxidil does not lead to new hair follicles. Instead new hair comes from existing quiescent terminal follicles and vellus follicles that have been revived. When the treatment is suspended, the follicles relapse to their previous state. This means that its use would be expensive, because it would have to be invested in throughout life. Furthermore there is evidence that it is most effective when dealing with baldness at an early stage. That means you need to start the minoxidil habit early on in life.

Minoxidil is not the only anti-hypertensive drug gathering interest in the hair-growing market. Another drug called 'Diazoxide', a potent vasodilator chemically unrelated to minoxidil, also stimulates hair growth, and plans are being made to develop it for the balding market.

The pharmaceutical and cosmetic companies would like to be able to market shampoos containing substances like minoxidil. This would allow the drug to be administered as part of a daily routine, and link its use with personal hygiene. The shampoo would also prime the scalp for the treatment by removing any build up of sebum and dandruff that might block the drug's absorption. Work is already underway to produce such a shampoo. There does not seem to be a problem in terms of minoxidil's stability inside the shampoo. Instead the stumbling block is that when you rinse off the shampoo it can get into your eyes, and the lather will certainly run down on to other parts of the body – with potentially embarrassing results. Work is underway to try to find a method to ensure that rinsings will contain a negligible amount of the drug.

The success of a pharmaceutical company in developing an anti-balding treatment has once again brought cosmetic companies face to face with the 'cosmeceutical'. Although some

companies cling to the hope that an innocuous potion of
vitamins will arrive and save the day, most of them realise that
the only way forward in the anti-baldness market is through
properly conducted clinical trials. If they choose not to take
that route they will have to leave this market to the pharmaceutical companies. Once consumers have started to buy
products whose claims have been substantiated in a hard
scientific trial, they are not going to return to products whose
claims are supported by insubstantial advertising copy.

Minoxidil is not a treatment that will work for everyone. But
for those scalps impervious to its effects there are other forms
of help at hand. Built on a solid base of male insecurity there are
plenty of techniques on offer to try to hide baldness. The oldest
and simplest method of hair transplantation is the autograft or
plug. The doctor plants on the patient's bald patch, by means
of an electric punch device, a crop of somewhere between 100
and 900 plugs consisting of seven to ten hairs each, taken from
the sides and the back of the head. It's a painstaking – and often
painful – operation, but it succeeds in its objective – at least
until the transplanted follicles close down. The only hazard
comes if your doctor is excessively neat and plants the plugs
geometrically so that you are left with the 'rows of corn' effect,
wherein your new hair looks as if it owes more to Massey
Ferguson than to surgery.

Men who lack enough hair to seed a bald patch have to resort
to what is known as scalp reduction surgery. A portion of the
bare scalp – typically about a centimetre wide – is cut out and
the rest of the scalp stretched to close the wound. After a few
more reductions and some judicious plugging, the bald patch
has disappeared. There are hazards. Sometimes the doctors
stretch the scalp too far and produce the 'chimpanzee look', in
which the patient's new hairline is so poorly engineered that it
almost merges into his eyebrows.

However there are some more promising routes being
studied. As we have seen, a bulb of epidermal cells at the base of
the follicle differentiates into a hair. But another type of cell – a
specialised fibroblast known as the dermal papilla – projects
into the bulbs and controls the production of the hair. Scientists have used this knowledge to devise a new method of hair
transplantation which could involve removing just a tiny piece

of hairy scalp. So far it has only been used on rats, but the results are promising.

Behind this new approach are researchers at Dundee University. Roy Oliver, Kenneth Horne and Colin Jahoda have removed tiny pieces of hairy skin from rats, isolated the dermal papillae and let them multiply in culture. They then transplanted these cells to inactive follicles in the snouts of the rats. The result was that the rats grew whiskers. Already Andrew Messenger, at Sheffield's Royal Hallamshire Hospital, has managed to culture dermal papilla cells from human hair follicles. What remains to be developed is a method for transplanting them back into the human scalp.

With the enticing prospect of using science to turn back the clock, many consumers are more than content for beauty to be only skin – or scalp – deep.

CHAPTER SEVEN

Lifestyles: Fuelling the Body

Our maximum possible lifespan is determined by the genes that we inherit – on average this figure is around 135 years. Of course, some individuals have the potential to reach the maximum because their particular set of genes is better at fighting disease and repairing the ravages of everyday life; others have drawn short straws and will fall victim to disease earlier in life.

However, this is no justification for fatalism. Whatever our potential lifespan, the age that we actually reach will be enormously influenced by the way in which we lead our lives. Many of the conditions normally associated with advancing age – heart disease and cancer, for example – have their roots in our lifestyles. Factors like smoking, excessive drinking, poor diet and lack of exercise can all cause enough damage to our bodies to ensure that it is these factors, and not our genes, that have the deciding say in how long we live.

The complexity of the battle for control between lifestyle and genes is starkly illustrated by the way in which super-fit health fanatics can die young, while some armchair athletes are able to smoke, drink, and happily defy the Grim Reaper. A healthy lifestyle does not necessarily guarantee a longer life, but it does mark the cards in your favour. No matter how expensive and sophisticated the treatment, there is no anti-ageing therapy that can repair the damage caused by a daily diet of saturated fat washed down with vast quantities of alcohol and finished off with a couple of packets of cigarettes.

As a people the British adopt a cynical attitude towards warnings from the health experts. There are plenty of unfit, overweight people who cling to the belief that health consciousness is for fanatics who have nothing better to do with their time. Living a healthy life is nothing short of hard work – and who wants to live longer if it means a bowl of bran for breakfast followed by a jog along the pavements half naked? In fact, as we will see in the next couple of chapters, a healthy lifestyle does not have to be hard work. On the whole, all that is required is 'moderation in all things'. Simple changes in the way we live can have dramatic effects.

Two hundred thousand people die from heart disease every year in Britain: more than one person every three minutes. Heart attacks are the main cause of death in this country, and also the most important cause of premature death: they claim 30 times as many victims as road accidents. The rates at which people are dying from heart disease in Scotland, Northern Ireland and Wales are now the highest in the world; England is not far behind. In the country as a whole heart disease has risen by three per cent among men and 10 per cent among women over the last 15 years. At the moment this increase seems to have levelled off, but it is still a disastrous state of affairs when compared with what has happened in other countries.

Over these same 15 years deaths linked to heart disease have fallen in the USA by 37 per cent; in Australia by 35 per cent; in New Zealand by 30 per cent; and in Canada by 26 per cent. The quality of medical care in these countries is much the same as in Britain. What has happened is that the people in these countries have become aware of the ways in which they can make their lifestyle healthier, and the results have been dramatic. These reductions are far greater than anything that could be achieved by doctors and hospitals. Nearly half of all heart attacks are fatal, and half of their victims are dead within 15 minutes, before medical help can even reach them. In fact, the provision of coronary care units in hospitals only decreases deaths by four or five per cent: this is a tribute to the skill of those who work in such units, but is nowhere near the reduction that could be achieved if the overall population changed its lifestyle.

Around 70,000 lives a year would be saved if Britain could cut the number of heart attacks by the same fraction as the Americans. At the moment the death toll in Britain is equivalent to nine fully laden jumbo jets crashing every week throughout the year. One-quarter of British men aged between 40 and 59 have some form of heart disease and the annual cost to the National Health Service is reckoned to be around 390 million pounds. Heart attacks are not just a male problem. They are the second most common cause of death in women up to the age of 54, and overall one in three people in Britain dies of a heart attack. Yet there is an international medical consensus as to how changes in lifestyle can slash the risk of heart disease.

A similarly depressing picture surrounds deaths from cancer. Every year more than 130,000 people in the UK die from some form of cancer, even though cancer specialists estimate that between 80 and 90 per cent of these deaths could have been avoided by a change in lifestyle.

In this chapter and the next we'll see how changing the way we live increases the chances of a long and healthy life. The starting point is diet, because the food and chemicals that we take into our bodies do much to determine just how vulnerable we are to disease, and in particular to the two great killers: heart disease and cancer.

The heart is a bag of muscle whose task is to pump blood to every part of the body. It takes in oxygen-rich blood from the lungs and then forces this blood through the arteries so that oxygen is delivered to every tissue in the body. This blood flows back to the heart through the veins, and is pumped back into the lungs to soak up more oxygen from the next breath of air that we take. The heart muscle contracts involuntarily, working day and night, beating about 70 times a minute. It has a tough job: each day it pumps the equivalent of seven tons of blood around the body.

Like all the other tissues in the body the heart needs to be supplied with oxygen-rich blood to stay alive. It receives this from tiny arteries which branch off from the aorta, the major artery through which the rest of the body's blood supply flows. These coronary arteries, as they are called, are the heart's private blood supply, feeding oxygen into the heart muscle. It is problems in these arteries which lie at the root of heart attacks: coronary heart disease is by far the commonest form of heart disease.

Coronary heart disease comes about because of the gradual narrowing of the coronary arteries, which anyway are not much thicker than a drinking straw. Fatty substances in the blood, including a substance called cholesterol, start to build up on the walls of the arteries. At first there are just isolated streaks of this material, but gradually these streaks merge into one another, and start to narrow the artery. This furring-up is called atherosclerosis, which literally means hardening of the arteries. The fatty material is called atheroma, from the Greek word for porridge.

Once the arteries start to narrow they are unable to deliver sufficient blood to the heart during times of high demand. When a muscle is deprived of sufficient blood supply it develops a cramp pain which is a signal for either less work or more oxygen. A heart muscle suffering from the effects of furred-up arteries reacts in the same way, although its pain signal is dignified with the name angina. Angina can be brought on by everyday activities such as walking up stairs or running for a train, or by emotions like excitement or anger. Hardly surprisingly, the stress of battling through crowds with a heavy suitcase means that airports and railway stations are often the scenes of the most violent angina attacks.

Many people cope with angina for years by avoiding over-exertion and using drugs which reduce the heart's need for oxygen or increase the amount of blood flowing to the heart. However, angina is a signal that you are on a slippery slope, with a higher than average risk of a heart attack.

The heart attack is a further stage in the progression of atherosclerosis – and many people who suffer heart attacks never have the warning of an angina attack. In the blood are special cells called platelets which control clotting when we cut ourselves. When these cells rub on the rough, scaly walls of an artery coated with atheroma they may become activated and form a blood clot or thrombosis.

If this clot is carried by the blood flow to a narrower, perhaps furred-up section of the artery it can clog the entire artery, so that the section of heart muscle served by that blood vessel has its blood supply cut off and dies, sending out a severe pain signal. This is what is meant by a 'coronary thrombosis' or 'coronary'. If the victim survives the dead muscle is replaced by scar tissue. However in many cases the clot may form near the beginning of the artery so that a great deal of muscle has its supply cut off, and the heart can no longer function. There may be an immediate failure of the entire heart (cardiac arrest), or it may occur up to 48 hours after the attack.

Sometimes a clot cannot be found in a post mortem. In these cases it is likely that the arteries become so narrow that the blood supply could not keep pace with the demands of the heart, and the heart simply stopped beating.

There is nothing inevitable about coronary heart disease. In fact, for our ancestors it was something of a curiosity. Angina was first described by an English doctor called Heberden in a paper presented to the Royal College of Physicians in London in 1768. At that time he had observed 20 cases. Eighteen years later he had seen only 100 people with the disease. Sir William Osler, who in 1892 was the most eminent doctor in Britain and America, described coronary heart disease as 'very rare'. During his long career he saw only a few dozen cases. Coronary heart disease is not a matter of bad luck: the decisive risk factors are under our own control.

The key factors which make us vulnerable to heart disease are high blood cholesterol, high blood pressure and smoking. There are other factors, but ultimately they can be reduced to the key factors. Increasing age, for example, brings a greater risk of a heart attack, because the furring-up of arteries begins in childhood, and so the chances of a heart attack increase with the passing of time. However, by taking action on the key risk factors you can slow down the furring of your arteries and minimise your risk. Hereditary factors may also increase your chances of a heart attack, because coronary heart disease does run in families. However, what you inherit is increased vulnerability to the key risk factors, which merely makes it even more important to take action to control them. As we will see in the next chapter, lack of exercise and too much stress are also culprits because of the way in which they affect blood pressure and cholesterol levels.

Even a moderately high level of cholesterol, blood pressure or smoking can double the risk of a heart attack. If you are at risk from more than one factor your chances of a heart attack spiral upwards because of the compound interest that governs the laws of chance: risk from two factors could mean a heart attack is four times more likely; risk from three can make it eight times more likely.

The driving force behind the present epidemic of heart disease is almost certainly the amount of fat in our food because of the way it can increase the level of cholesterol in our blood and accelerate the narrowing of our coronary arteries. Two-thirds of the adults in Britain run an increased risk of heart disease because the level of cholesterol in their blood is higher than the 200 milligrams per litre recommended by the World Health Organisation. One in four people have cholesterol levels which are high enough to double their chances of a heart attack.

It has long intrigued scientists that although heart disease is widespread in countries like Britain and the USA, it is a limited threat in countries like Japan. Even though the Japanese have the highest rate of cigarette smoking in the world, a high average blood pressure and a stressful lifestyle, their protection from heart disease is greater than ours. The answer to this conundrum appears to lie in the large amounts of fish and vegetables in the Japanese diet. Meat and dairy products are scarce, and only 15 per cent of the total calories eaten by the average Japanese come from fat; in Britain that figure stands at 38 per cent. The influence of diet on health is seen when Japanese people emigrate to Hawaii or California. If they take to an American high-fat diet of hamburgers and French fries, they also acquire the American rate of coronary heart disease (and the American rate of bowel and breast cancer).

However, it is not just the quantity of fat in the diet that matters, but also the type of fat. In northern Europe and North America the incidence of heart disease is much higher than in the Mediterranean countries. The main difference in the diet of these regions is the type of fat that people eat. Animal fats go down well in the northern heart attack zones, while in the Mediterranean people opt more for fish and poultry, and use vegetable oils rather than fats for cooking in. It is a difference which is the key to understanding how fat is linked with heart disease.

Most animal fats contain large amounts of substances called 'saturated' fats (broken down in the body into saturated fatty acids). Fish, poultry and vegetables are high in 'polyun-saturated' fats (broken down into polyunsaturated fatty acids).

Saturated and unsaturated are adjectives used by chemists to describe the number of hydrogen atoms that surround the carbon atoms in the fat. Unsaturated fats have fewer hydrogen atoms than saturated fats. This chemical difference means that saturated fats are usually solid at room temperature, while unsaturated fats are usually liquid. Most scientists agree that the more saturated fat you eat the higher the level of cholesterol in the blood, and the greater the risk of developing heart disease. Eating polyunsaturated fat *decreases* the total cholesterol in the blood.

Cholesterol has an important role to play in the normal, healthy working of our bodies because it is one of the raw materials for making hormones and cell membranes. However, if too much cholesterol is circulating in the blood then some of the excess can be absorbed by the walls of the blood vessels, particularly the coronary arteries. This excess cholesterol can build up into the fatty material which narrows the arteries and increases the chances of a heart attack.

A 1987 American study has ended years of controversy by providing definitive proof that a large reduction in blood cholesterol levels will slow and even reverse these fatty deposits which play such an important role in provoking heart attacks. Scientists at the University of Southern California Medical School used drugs to dramatically lower the levels in a group of non-smoking men who had already suffered clogged arteries and had undergone bypass surgery in which veins are stitched in to replace the coronary arteries. After two years of treatment X-ray films were used to investigate the state of their arteries. Sixteen per cent of those on the drug treatment showed a discernible shrinkage in fatty deposits, as opposed to just over two per cent in a control group. Only 39 per cent of those being treated showed a worsening of their arterial clogging, compared with 61 per cent in the control group. Other scientists are now starting out on fresh studies to see if different drugs and diet, together with a longer period of treatment, can better these figures.

Cholesterol is widely distributed in nature and is particularly abundant in egg yolks and 'organ' meats such as liver, kidney and brain. However, most people can eat comparatively large amounts of cholesterol without any harmful build up in the blood stream. This is because about 80 per cent of the cholesterol in a normal person's bloodstream comes not from their diet but from the liver where the body manufactures its own supply of cholesterol. The rate of manufacture does not always remain constant; if a diet is high in cholesterol the liver can cut back its own production of cholesterol in order to compensate, but often not by enough to prevent the level of cholesterol in the blood from rising. The liver can also step up production if not enough cholesterol is provided in the diet.

There is another class of substance that along with cholesterol may play a key part in the development of heart disease. Cholesterol is insoluble in blood and has to be carried round the body by tailor-made carriers called lipoproteins. There are three types of lipoproteins – high-density lipoproteins (HDLs), low-density lipoproteins (LDLs) and very low-density lipoproteins (VDLs). Low-density lipoproteins are responsible for transporting cholesterol from the liver to the blood vessels. High-density lipoproteins do the exact opposite to LDLs and transport cholesterol from the blood vessels to the liver where the cholesterol is broken down.

By balancing HDLs and LDLs our body keeps the blood flowing freely through the coronary arteries to the heart while allowing cells to get as much cholesterol as they need. Increased levels of LDL have been linked to an increased risk of coronary heart disease in several studies. One extreme example of this correlation is the high incidence of premature death from coronary heart disease in people suffering from familial hypocholesterolaemia, an inherited disease in which blood LDL concentrations increase dramatically. There is also evidence that LDLs are attracted to areas where a blood vessel is damaged, or a clot is formed, further helping to create the conditions needed for a coronary thrombosis.

Not surprisingly, some studies have found signs that high levels of HDLs are linked with lower rates of heart disease. However work carried out at London's Royal Free Hospital in 1986 found that although HDL levels were low in men who had already suffered heart attacks, the variation was not significant. This study came to the conclusion that the best way to predict the risk of a heart attack is to look at the ratio of HDLs and LDLs, not just their individual levels.

The discovery of the HDL/LDL mechanism won Michael Brown and Joseph Goldstein of the University of Texas the Nobel prize for medicine in 1985, and it has now been used to develop a drug called Lovastin which can control the level of cholesterol in our blood. The drug stops the liver from making cholesterol by interfering with one of the key steps in the manufacturing process. As a result the liver manufactures more HDLs which scour the body for extra cholesterol and bring it to the liver, lowering the level of cholesterol in the blood.

For the moment Lovastin's long-term safety is not clear, and it is not a substitute for switching to a healthier diet. The US Government, which has issued guidelines to doctors on how to lower cholesterol levels, says that drugs should only be used in extreme cases (although some Wall Street analysts have estimated that Lovastin will bring Merck, the company that makes the drug, sales of more than one billion dollars a year).

It is still far from clear whether cutting down cholesterol in the diet benefits people with normal levels of HDLs and LDLs. A number of studies have suggested that restricting dietary cholesterol makes little difference to people with high blood levels of cholesterol (they would probably do better to rely on drug therapies) and is simply irrelevant for those with average cholesterol levels (because most of that cholesterol comes from the liver). The amount of saturated fat in our diet has a far greater influence on the overall level of cholesterol in our blood than the amount of cholesterol we eat. We need to worry about cutting out saturated fat, not cholesterol, from our diet.

Most medical experts agree that a diet low in saturated fat reduces the risk of dying from a heart attack. In 1984, the UK Government's advisory committee on medical aspects of food policy (COMA) advised that most people should limit their intake of saturated fats (which very largely means animal fats) to no more than 15 per cent of their daily food energy intake. At the moment the average person in the UK gets about 23 per cent of their daily energy from saturated fats, foods rich in animal fat such as red meat, milk and cheese. A 1983 discussion paper prepared for the British National Advisory Committee on Nutrition Education went even further, recommending that saturated fats should make up no more than 10 per cent of the total energy intake. They also recommended that people should reduce their total fat intake to 30 per cent of energy intake, instead of the current 38 per cent.

Cutting the intake of saturated fat and increasing the proportion of polyunsaturated fat in the food that you do eat, will reduce the level of cholesterol in the blood. This means that you are less likely to have a heart attack, because your coronary arteries are less likely to become furred up.

According to the British Government's national food survey, about one-quarter of the saturated fat in our diet comes from meat and meat products; one-quarter from cream, milk and cheese; one-quarter from butter and margarine; one-tenth from cooking oils and fats; and one-sixth from convenience foods and snacks like chocolate and crisps.

Start by trying to avoid factory prepared pies and sausages. These tend to be particularly high in fat because fat is cheaper than meat, and the food manufacturers tend to stretch their meat with it. Red meat is high in fat – a roast leg of pork is 20 per cent fat, a roast shoulder of lamb 26 per cent fat – and so you should try to eat it less often. Furthermore, about half the fat in red meat is saturated. Instead of red meat you could try eating more chicken, which has less fat and a lower proportion of saturated fat. Fish contain even less fat and, in the case of oily fish like herring and mackerel, are high in polyunsaturates.

Cheese can contain a lot of fat, and two-thirds of it is saturated. However picking cheese with care solves the problem. Cream cheese is 50 per cent fat, most Cheddars are around 33 per cent fat, while soft cheeses like Camembert and Brie are 23 per cent fat. Cottage cheese contains just four per cent fat.

Butter is around 80 per cent fat, of which two-thirds is saturated. Margarine contains about the same amount of fat, but, depending on the margarine, only 20 to 40 per cent of this fat is saturated. The sensible thing is to switch to a margarine labelled 'high in polyunsaturates' or 'high in essential polyunsaturates'. Margarines not labelled in this way contain only a little less saturated fat than butter. In addition, there are now low-fat spreads containing around half the fat of butter on the market.

Milk is about four per cent fat, two-thirds of which is saturated. The total level of fat is low, but because most people drink a lot of milk (even if it is only in tea) it is a major source of fat in the diet. Even half-a-pint a day is the equivalent in terms of fat to sitting down and drinking a pint of single cream every week. It's a fairly easy matter to switch to semi-skimmed milk (which has half the fat) or skimmed milk (which has no fat). They both have the same amounts of calcium and protein as ordinary milk. Cream is high in fat and should be saved for special occasions.

Finally cooking oils and cooking fats account for around one-tenth of fat intake. Try to cut down the amount of fried food you eat and switch to vegetable oil for cooking. Corn oil, groundnut oil, olive oil and soya oil have only about 20 per cent saturated fat. Sunflower oil is only 15 per cent saturated.

Snack and convenience foods account for one-sixth of fat intake. Crisps, chocolates, biscuits, cakes and pastry products are all high in fat – and often high in saturated fats.

It seems important to get the right balance of saturated and unsaturated fat in the diet because although too much saturated fat can cause heart disease, Professor Michael Oliver from Edinburgh has discovered that too little unsaturated fat can also be dangerous. He discovered that the high levels of heart disease in Scotland are statistically linked to low levels of an unsaturated fat called linoleic acid.

Linoleic acid is essential for the formation of vital chemicals called prostaglandins, and it also controls the permeability of cell membranes. Since linoleic acid cannot be synthesised in the body, all the linoleic acid needed to carry out these processes must come from our diet. International studies suggest that those countries with a high mortality rate from coronary disease do tend to have populations with low levels of linoleic acid in their bodies. Luckily it is very easy to ensure that our diets contain linoleic acid since it is the most common unsaturated fatty acid and is found in corn, soya and sunflower oils, fish, game, poultry and cereals.

There may be other compelling reasons to increase our intake of fish oils. Researchers in the Netherlands recently released the results of a 20-year study which found that fatal heart attacks were 50 per cent less likely among middle-aged men who ate at least an ounce of fish every day. More evidence comes from investigations into the Eskimo diet which showed that although 40 per cent of an Eskimo's energy intake is in the form of fatty fish, they suffer very little heart disease.

The explanation for this phenomenon is that many fish are rich in a fatty acid called eicosapentaenoic acid (EPA), which is used in the body to prevent the formation of blood clots. Control over blood clotting has to be very finely tuned because if blood clots form where they are not needed, for example in the coronary arteries, the results are likely to be fatal.

Clots are formed when blood clotting cells called platelets clump together with the aid of an adhesive chemical called thromboxane; if too much thromboxane is present it becomes easier for the platelets to clump together to form blood clots. The platelets in an Eskimo's blood are far less sticky than those in a red meat eater, and the linings of their blood vessels are far smoother and so less likely to accept little clumps of platelets. The net result is that Eskimos are unlikely to suffer from heart attacks and strokes. The EPA in the Eskimo diet neutralises the action of thromboxane by forming an anti-coagulant called prostacyclin on the lining of the blood vessels. This keeps them smooth and free of sticky platelets.

It isn't necessary to follow an Eskimo diet of blubber to increase EPA intake. All that is needed is to include fatty fish like salmon, tuna, mackerel and herrings in our diets. Shellfish like lobsters and shrimps are not very beneficial because they are low in EPA. Ultimately, there is enormously strong scientific evidence that if you cut down the total amount of fat you eat, and increase the proportion of polyunsaturated to saturated fat, you will decrease your chances of a heart attack.

High blood pressure is another of the key factors which predisposes the body to a heart attack. People whose blood pressure is very high are four times more likely to suffer a heart attack than people with normal blood pressure.

Blood pressure is the pressure exerted by the heart and arteries to force blood through the body. A high blood pressure puts a strain on the heart and damages the lining of the arteries, making it easier for them to fur up.

High blood pressure is quite normal during exercise, or when we are afraid, or angry or excited. The rise in blood pressure is brought about by hormones like adrenaline, which make the heart pump harder to deliver extra blood and oxygen to the muscles and brain. This is the 'fight or flight' mechanism which is common to all animals, and gives us the extra energy to get ourselves out of danger. Once the situation which has provoked the increase has passed, blood pressure returns to normal.

What is much more dangerous is that many people have high blood pressure when they are not under any stress, but simply reading or watching television. It is this condition, which doctors refer to as hypertension, which greatly increases the risk of damage to the coronary arteries and of heart attack. It can be treated with drugs, but most high blood pressure comes about because of the way we live.

One of the commonest causes of high blood pressure is being overweight. A 1983 report commissioned by the Royal College of Surgeons revealed that one in every three adults in the UK is overweight, as well as one in twenty children. An overweight person's heart and arteries have to strain away coping with a body that is much larger than they were designed to cope with. You are carrying too much weight if you are more than 10 pounds heavier than you were when you were 20 (assuming that you were still slim and beautiful at this early age!). Your doctor or the Health Education Authority can supply you with a chart showing what your ideal weight should be.

Even being mildly overweight increases blood pressure and the risk of a heart attack. This risk is multiplied because overweight people also have higher blood cholesterol levels. It also increases the risk of gall bladder disease and diabetes. Obese men, regardless of smoking habits, have higher rates of colon, rectal and prostate cancer. Obese women stand a greater chance of death from cancer of the gall bladder, breasts, ovaries and uterus. (The medical profession labels anyone who is 20 per cent or more over their ideal weight as 'obese'.)

All overweight people have one thing in common – they eat more food than they need to fuel their bodies. The laws of thermodynamics dictate that whenever energy intake exceeds energy output the excess has to be stored somewhere – and in the body that means fat. But where that fat is stored can be critical. Recent research in the USA and Sweden suggests that fat stores around the abdomen are particularly dangerous because they release large amounts of fatty acids into the bloodstream. Men are particularly prone to 'abdominal obesity' because they tend to deposit excess fat around their middles. As well as looking very unappealing this way of storing fat may explain why once a man's 'beer gut' flops over his trousers his risk of heart disease increases sharply. Women tend to escape this problem because they usually gain weight on their thighs and hips.

The only way to lose weight is to alter the balance between intake and output, by either taking in less energy by changing the diet, or by burning up more energy through exercise. The remedy sounds simple, but because our expectations are unrealistic the results are often frustrating.

The speed at which we can lose our excess fat depends upon factors like our age, sex and basal metabolic rate. The basal metabolic rate (BMR) measures the amount of energy the body burns to keep itself ticking over, usually about 60 per cent of the body's energy needs. If you are unlucky enough to have inherited a low BMR then without extra exercise you will gain weight when a person with a higher BMR will stay the same or even lose weight. Some simple arithmetic makes it clear why dieting is so difficult. If your body normally runs at 2,000 calories a day, a diet of 1,500 calories a day leaves your body 3,500 calories short over a week, and so your body is forced to make up the difference by burning some fat. Unfortunately for slimmers, 3,500 calories can be stored in less than a pound of fat.

Losing weight by eating less is a slow business, and it is hardly surprising that many people are tempted by miracle diets which promise fast and dramatic weight loss. Unfortunately, despite what the authors of these regimes may promise, there is no way of cheating the laws of thermodynamics. Even crash dieting is not very useful for long-term weight loss. The initial weight loss in the first week can be up to 11 pounds, but only 10 per cent of this will be body fat, with the rest consisting of water, glycogen and muscle. Furthermore, crash dieting can have disastrous consequences, as seen in the case of sufferers of anorexia nervosa. All women who lose too much weight can become infertile, and sufferers from anorexia nervosa pass through a threshold ratio of body weight to volume and stop menstruating. It is much more sensible to try to safely alter the diet instead of relying on rapid weight loss to bring you back into shape.

Most people are overweight because they take in unnecessary calories by eating too much fat and sugar. We have already seen how to cut down on fat – and as an extra stimulus evidence has now emerged that people who eat a lot of fat have slower metabolic rates, making it even more likely that they will be overweight.

On average we eat around 80 pounds of sugar a year, half of this coming from sugar that we add to food ourselves. Unlike saturated fats, sugar is not especially bad for your heart, but it is an important reason why many of us are overweight. It consists of 'empty calories' in that it contains no nutrients of any kind, and is no better at delivering energy than any other type of food. The guidelines suggested by the National Advisory Council on Nutrition Education recommend that we should cut our annual sugar consumption by about half. In fact there is no reason why you should not go further. Giving up sugar may seem unthinkable if you have a sweet tooth. However, anyone who has given up sugar in, say, tea or coffee will tell you that you soon forget its absence.

The reasons why some people become overweight more easily may be explained by chemical processes inside our cells. One explanation is the 'brown fat theory', which proposes that some people gain weight because they are unable to burn up excess food and dissipate it in the form of heat. Animals tend to turn up the body's thermostat when they eat. It has been discovered that in mice this process takes place in a particular type of tissue surrounding the neck, ribs and kidneys, called brown fat. It seems that this type of fat may have more to do with helping you slim than putting on weight. These fat cells are brown because they are filled with huge numbers of sausage-shaped objects called mitochondria. Like white fat cells, brown fat cells store fat in the form of droplets. However, in brown fat cells the mitochondria act like small furnaces, burning the fat droplets to produce heat and keep the animal warm in cold weather.

Brown fat was discovered in the 1960s when scientists realised that new-born babies do not need to shiver to keep warm because they have large amounts of brown fat cells which can boost their central heating. It was some time later that British scientists discovered that rats who put on weight have low levels of brown fat cells. It seemed that this lack of brown fat could be responsible for the increased weight of these rats.

The theory is attractive, but it may be a little too neat. Adult humans, whether fat or thin, seem to have only small amounts of brown fat cells, although they may be mixed in within the ordinary white fat cells, making them difficult to spot.

Since these findings were first published, a great deal of research has focused on trying to stimulate the brown fat cells in obese people so that excess fat can be burnt off as waste heat. British scientists at Beechams' Research Laboratories in the UK were particularly interested in finding a drug which would stimulate the brown fat cells without causing harmful side effects throughout the rest of the body. In 1984 they succeeded. They solved the problem by exploiting the natural way in which the mitochondria inside brown fat cells of a normal individual are switched on.

In a naturally thin person, the first signs of a food surplus cause a chemical called noradrenaline to be released. This acts like a chemical key, fitting into the lock or receptor on the outside of the brown fat cell. This triggers a chain reaction inside the cell which starts up the fat-burning process inside the mitochondria. As long as noradrenaline is produced by the body, fat will be used as fuel by the mitochondria. Fat is moved from other parts of the body to replace the fat droplets that have been burnt in the brown fat cell, and so the body's weight is kept under control.

In obese people this process does not work properly. Not enough noradrenaline is released by the body to stimulate the mitochondria and the brown fat cells shrivel up. In their search for a drug which would redress the balance, scientists at Beechams knew that noradrenaline itself could not be prescribed as a cure for obesity because this chemical has profound effects on the way the heart, lungs and blood vessels operate. Success came when the scientists were able to copy just the specific part of the noradrenaline molecule that fits into the lock on a brown fat cell. This drug is now being tested in clinical trials, and if it is as effective in humans as it seems to be in mice, then in a few years time there may be pills available to grossly obese people to help them lose weight without starving themselves.

In the meantime research into the brown fat theory has thrown up extra evidence about the benefits of a low-fat diet. It seems that some obese people are better able to dissipate extra calories as heat if they take their calories in the form of protein and starch, implying that weight control is best achieved by a low-fat diet.

Being overweight is not the only factor that scientists have investigated as a cause of high blood pressure. There has been enormous controversy, particularly in the USA, over the role of common salt, sodium chloride, in raising blood pressure.

A new question being asked at American dinner parties over the past few years is 'are you a saltaholic?' If 'yes' is the answer, then the American food industry can help by offering a variety of fast-selling salt substitutes. The world of publishing has joined the salt hype with titles like *Killer Salt* and *Shake the Salt Habit*, all designed to instil a sense of guilt. But other than making us feel guilty about our eating habits is there any scientific basis for this American obsession with sodium chloride?

There is little doubt that salt does push up the blood pressure in people who already suffer from raised blood pressure or hypertension. Most doctors agree that hypertensives should reduce their salt intake, but so far there is controversy as to whether salt raises blood pressure in people who are not hypertensive. It is an important argument because hypertension is closely associated with heart disease and strokes.

As well as being a vital part of a normal diet, its value has been recognised throughout history. Roman soldiers were sometimes given part of their pay as salt – the word salary derives from the Latin word for salt, *salsus*.

Inside the body sodium chloride is important because it regulates blood volume and controls the movement of water in and out of cells. It is also one of the main chemicals used to facilitate the passage of nerve impulses between the cells. The healthy body needs and can use only about 0.4 grams of salt each day, and anything more should be excreted by the kidneys. In Britain we eat, on average, somewhere between eight and ten grams per day – about two teaspoons' worth. About three grams come from the natural salt content of foods, four grams are added by the food processors, and we add an additional three grams ourselves. Similar figures hold for most of Europe and the USA. There is no doubt that we eat far more salt than we require. The question that has to be answered is whether this does us any harm.

The exact link between large amounts of salt in the diet and high blood pressure is not fully understood, but at Charing Cross Hospital in London researchers have come up with a possible explanation. They believe that in hypertensives, large amounts of salt in the diet trigger the release of a hormone called renin from the brain. This hormone is transported to the kidneys to speed up the removal of salt. Unfortunately, this hormone also travels around the rest of the body where it has an unwanted side effect. It acts on the blood vessels, making them constrict. This means that the heart has to work against greater resistance, and to keep the circulation going, blood pressure rises.

Controlling hypertension by cutting salt consumption is a much tougher affair than drug therapy. For a patient with high blood pressure to feel any benefit he must reduce his daily salt consumption to one gram. That means eliminating virtually all canned food, sauces, processed meat, cheese and smoked foods. Not many people could face this way of life.

The notion that salt causes high blood pressure in normal people stems from two studies carried out some 20 years ago. The large numbers of hypertensives among the residents of northern Japan was linked to their preference for a salty fish diet, and the low incidence of high blood pressure in some Solomon Island tribes to a low salt diet. It is now recognised that many other factors can account for such differences between cultures. For example, Solomon Islanders tend to be small and thin and there is now known to be a significant link between blood pressure and body weight. Subsequent population studies which have taken body weight into account have found that this accounts for most, but not all, of the differences in blood pressure between different nationalities.

In fact scientists now suspect that salt only raises blood pressure in healthy people when it is coupled with a diet low in potassium or calcium. However, much more work needs to be done to prove these hypotheses, and for the moment there is no compelling reason why people with normal blood pressure should cut down on salt. But if you follow the adage of moderation in all things, you might consider cutting down. Anyone who has cut down on salt will tell you that after a while food tastes just as 'salty' even though far less salt is added. If your body only needs 0.4 grams of salt a day, why eat 10 grams a day?

On the whole the only exception to the adage 'moderation in all things' is tobacco. It has no saving grace when used in even the most sparing of amounts. Of course some smokers do live to a great age, but they do so despite tobacco, not because of it. We tend to credit their achievement in reaching old age with disproportionate attention because we are still able to meet and talk with them. Most smokers die earlier than they would have if they did not smoke. They are not around to scoff at the warnings about the dangers from smoking.

Cancer is not the only way that tobacco kills, nor is it even the most important. The British Regional Heart Study Group, which monitors a group of 7,735 middle-aged men in 24 towns in Britain, found that the *major* cause of decreased life expectancy among smokers is heart disease.

The statistics which link heart disease with smoking are extraordinary. Most of the younger victims of heart attacks are smokers. One famous study into the smoking habits of British doctors considered men who smoked more than 25 cigarettes a day. It found that those under 45 years of age were 15 times more likely to die of a heart attack than non-smokers; those between 45 and 54 were three times as likely to have a fatal heart attack; and those aged 55 to 64 were twice as likely to die from a heart attack.

The risk of a heart attack depends on the number of cigarettes smoked each day. Twenty cigarettes a day triples the chances, while 40 or more cigarettes increases the probability

LIFESTYLES: FUELLING THE BODY

of a heart attack by a factor of 20. The odds are further stacked against smokers in that they are more likely to have *fatal* heart attacks.

The study also made some other unexpected findings, all of which serve to show the dangers of tobacco. When researchers used the group to assess the risk of heart disease among former smokers, they discovered that the number of years a man has smoked cigarettes is more important in determining his risk from heart disease than the number of years it is since he gave up smoking. Until this study, it had always been assumed that men under the age of 65 who had not smoked for 10 years had reduced their risk of heart disease to that of non-smokers. This study showed that a man who has given up smoking for 10 years is twice as likely to suffer heart disease as someone who has never smoked. Even after 20 years his risk will still be substantially higher than if he had never smoked.

One of the reasons for the faster rise in rates of heart disease among women in Britain is that women are smoking more cigarettes than they used to. In the past it was often thought that cigarette smoking had less of an impact on coronary heart disease among women. This is not true. In America the results of the largest-ever study on the effects of smoking on heart disease risks amongst women have just been published. This survey monitored the health of 120,000 nurses. It found that even the lightest smokers, those who smoke just one to four cigarettes a day, increase their chances of a heart attack by between two to three times. Tobacco was the cause of about 60 per cent of the heart disease among light smokers; among the heaviest smokers that figure jumps to 90 per cent. The study was unable to identify any situation in which smoking did not increase the risk of heart disease.

The nicotine and carbon monoxide in cigarette smoke have a direct effect on the heart. These chemicals do not just wreak havoc in the lungs; they are also absorbed into the bloodstream and travel throughout the body. Nicotine has the effect of constricting the coronary arteries so that the amount of blood reaching the heart is restricted; at the same time it increases the heart's oxygen requirements. As a result blood pressure and heart rate both increase. Carbon monoxide makes matters worse by binding with haemoglobin, the chemical that carries oxygen around in the blood. As a result the blood reaching the heart muscle through the coronary arteries contains less oxygen.

Cigarette smoking also decreases the ratio of high-density lipoproteins to low-density lipoproteins in the blood, with the result that the furring up of the coronary arteries is greatly accelerated. To cap this, cigarette smoking also makes the platelets in our blood more liable to clot, creating a perfect breeding ground for coronary thrombosis.

There is no safe level of smoking. It is not even true that cigarettes deliver some benefit by keeping down your weight. It is a myth that everyone who stops smoking puts on weight, and whatever weight you might put on would be a tiny risk to your health compared with the danger from smoking. You would have to put on at least 10 stones in weight to increase your chances of heart disease by the same factor as 20 cigarettes a day.

Smoking and the food we eat do not just affect how much heart disease we suffer. They also do much to determine whether or not we will suffer from cancer. Cancer is the cause of between a fifth and a quarter of all deaths, and a third of all natural deaths. But it is not an indiscriminate disease; there are discernible patterns. Smoking is the cause of nearly a third of all cancers. A further third are related to other factors in our diet, principally too much fat and too little fibre.

A 1985 report by the Health Education Council and the British Medical Association showed that every year in England and Wales smoking kills around 55,000 men and 23,000 women, and puts 108,000 in hospital with heart disease, lung cancer, bronchitis and emphysema. The report estimated that since 1945 around 3 million people in England and Wales have been killed by smoking, and that a further 1.5 million will die by the year 2000 if there is no change in smoking habits. In 1984 34 per cent of the population aged over 16 smoked, with 36 per cent of men smoking as compared with 32 per cent of women. (In 1972 52 per cent of adult men smoked compared with 41 per cent of adult women.)

In America tobacco could be directly responsible for more than 300,000 deaths every year; cigarette smoking causes more premature deaths than AIDS, heroin, cocaine, alcohol, car accidents, murder and suicide added together. Based on these figures, in May 1984, the US Surgeon General issued a call for a 'smoke-free' society by the year 2000 because 'smoking is the chief, single, avoidable cause of death in our society'. In 1980, more than 30 per cent of American adults smoked. By the end of 1986 that figure had fallen to 27 per cent (29.5 per cent of men and 24 per cent of women). The National Cancer Institute hopes to reduce this to 24 per cent by 1990 and 15 per cent by the turn of the century. According to researchers at the NCI, even if all smokers gave up tobacco today, there would still be cancer deaths occurring after the year 2000 as a result of tobacco.

The link between tobacco and lung cancer has been exhaustively probed and is now accepted by the medical profession almost without question. However, the reality has yet to get through to those who smoke; it is estimated that nearly one-third of cancer deaths in Britain would be prevented if people gave up cigarettes. Men who smoke a packet of cigarettes every day are ten times more likely to get lung cancer than a non-smoker. Smoking two packets a day increases this figure to 25.

Smokers do not just increase their personal risk from lung cancer. The Independent Scientific Committee on Smoking and Health, a group sponsored by the British Government, recently reported that non-smokers are between 10 and 30 per cent more likely to get lung cancer if they are consistently exposed to other people's tobacco smoke. A review of 13 worldwide studies showed that a quarter of the cases of lung cancer in non-smokers could be attributed to 'passive' smoking – inhaling someone else's tobacco smoke. In fact the smoke coming off the end of a lit cigarette contains higher concentrations of many toxic chemicals than the smoke smokers take into their lungs. The children of parents who smoke are far more prone to chest infections.

Smoking used to be seen as a man's problem, but it is now becoming a woman's issue. In 1984 more women aged 16 to 19 smoked than did men of the same age; 32 per cent compared with 29 per cent. Although lung cancer during the last 20 years has been declining slightly among men under the age of 65, it is still on the increase among women, and if present trends continue it will overtake breast cancer as the leading cancer killer among British women by the year 2010 (now less than 25 years away!). This has already happened in Scotland. Recent studies have also pinpointed smoking as a possible cause of cervical cancer.

To add insult to injury, a recent American study, which monitored 50,000 women, found that women who smoke accelerate the rate at which their skin starts to wrinkle. As we mentioned in chapter six, scientists have long speculated that chemicals called free radicals which are present in cigarette smoke initiate cross-linking which leads to loss of elasticity in the skin and to wrinkles. It seems fairly certain that anyone who smokes is wasting their time buying any of the current anti-ageing skin treatments. Cigarette smoke delivers enough dangerous chemicals to completely swamp these delicate potions.

Men may not worry about wrinkles, but they might be concerned about the new research which suggests that smoking can cause impotence in middle-aged men, a finding that does not sit comfortably with those advertising campaigns which try to promote smoking as sexy.

The only advice as far as smoking is concerned is – give it up. Tobacco will almost certainly shorten your life, and will wipe out any other steps you are taking to try to live a longer, healthier life.

One dietary theory suggests that eating too much fat increases the risk of cancer of the colon, breast and prostate. Though studied extensively the theory has never been tested in a clinical trial: you cannot cram people full of fat to see if they develop cancer! Instead scientists have had to rely on statistical studies to see if a cause and effect relationship exists.

The earliest indicators that fat might be involved in cancer came from the simple observation that in Japan, where, as we have seen, only a small fraction of the calories in the traditional diet come from fat, breast cancer is comparatively rare. However in countries like Britain and the USA breast cancer is a leading killer.

When a team of British scientists studied a group of vegetarian nuns who ate less fat than the rest of the population, they found no difference in their cancer rate. So far scientists have been unable to uncover a simple link between fat consumption and cancer in humans.

If fat in the diet is one of the major causes of certain types of cancer, then the way in which it brings it about has to be uncovered. Back in 1969 a team of British scientists proposed that the fat in our diet stimulates the production of substances known as bile acids and sterols. These chemicals are believed to have the ability to cause tumours in the colon. However, this explanation is no substitute for the firm statistical link that exists, for example, between cigarette smoking and lung cancer.

Nevertheless, in the USA, the National Research Council and the National Cancer Institute have enough confidence in the link between dietary fat and cancer to recommend women to cut down on fat so that it accounts for no more than 30 per cent of the calories they take in. This, says the Institute, will reduce their risk of contracting breast cancer. This is something of a tall order, because at the moment the average American woman consumes 40 per cent of her calories as fat.

Carbohydrates, once considered to be 'fattening', are now encouraged as part of a healthy diet because they contain large amounts of 'fibre'. Although 'fibre' has become a buzz word synonymous with health foods and diets, it is simply the building material from which plants are made. Before its meteoric rise to fame it was thought to have little nutritional value because the enzymes in the gut were unable to digest it. For years food processors and manufacturers in the industrialised countries 'refined' foods like sugar, flour and rice to remove fibre.

Ironically, during the food shortages in Britain during the Second World War, wheat was in such short supply that milling techniques had to be radically altered, with the result that everyone was forced to eat unrefined brown bread – and was much healthier for it. Unfortunately, as a mark of postwar wealth, refined white bread returned along with refined carbohydrates like white sugar, white flour and white rice.

Evidence is accumulating that some of the medical problems which are common in industrialised countries, but rare in

Third World countries, are linked to the amount of fibre that people eat. Most nutrition experts now believe that eating more fibre has a direct effect on our health by reducing the risk of cancer of the colon, heart disease, and diabetes. Rates of colon cancer tend to be high in countries like ours where fat consumption is high, and fibre consumption low.

The fibre that we eat in our diets comes from the cell walls of plants, and consists of sugars called polysaccharides. Since there are many different types of fibre, there are many different types of polysaccharides. They are usually divided into two groups: cellulose and non-cellulosic polysaccharides.

When fibre is eaten the cellulose tends to survive digestion better than the non-cellulosic polysaccharides. Fibre from cereals survives better than that from vegetables and fruit. For example, when the digestion of cabbage fibre was compared with that of bran, 90 per cent of the cabbage was digested compared with just 40 per cent of the bran. The largely indigestible plant cells from bran hold water as they travel through the gut, increasing the bulk of the faecal waste and pushing it though faster. All types of fibre stimulate the growth of the millions of bacteria that live in the colon. As they grow they also make the faeces bulkier, again with the result that the whole waste disposal system is speeded up. Ths is important because the longer that waste stays in the body, the longer the body is exposed to potential carcinogens in the faeces.

The non-cellulosic types of fibre are almost completely broken down in the gut into chemicals called short-chain fatty acids. Recent evidence suggests that one of these acids, butanoic acid, may help protect the bowel against cancer. It can certainly prevent the growth of tumours in the laboratory, but it is too early to say whether it can perform the same anti-cancer role inside the body.

However, this work in the laboratory is supported by a statistical study which showed that men and women who die from bowel cancer in Britain tend to have a low-fibre diet. It does seem that a high-fibre diet gives significant protection against bowel cancer.

Furthermore, increasing the amount of fibre in the diet lowers the level of cholesterol in the blood, reducing the risk of heart disease. It seems that fibre can protect us against both the major killers of our time.

Some scientists claim that high-fibre diets could interfere with the gut's ability to absorb minerals. For example, bran contains a chemical which is known to be able to interfere with the absorption of calcium in the body. In the pregnant or elderly it is possible that calcium levels could be critical, and so it might be advisable for them to eat other types of fibre.

For the moment it seems that fat and fibre are the foods most closely linked with cancer. However in the USA the National Cancer Institute have just embarked on a number of large population studies to test links with various nutrients, such as vitamins A, C and E, although it will be many years before the verdict will be in.

There have been attempts to reproduce a Third World diet which is high in fibre, low in fat and salt, and involves no alcohol or tobacco. One such diet is now on offer to affluent Californians who can afford eight thousand dollars to attend the Pritikin Longevity Center in Santa Monica. The diet is based around Nathan Pritikin's seven commandments: thou shalt not smoke, eat fat, sugar, salt or drink tea, coffee or alcohol. One of the major aims of the diet is to reduce the risk of heart disease, and so it derives only 10 per cent of its calories from fat, with a further 10 per cent from protein and 80 per cent from carbohydrates. Some members of the scientific community are sceptical about how much can be achieved in such a short time, but the diet could be a means to extending life expectancy.

One British doctor has given a similar diet his approval by administering it – apparently successfully – to patients with angina and diabetes. Like Nathan Pritikin, Dr Paul Dodson designed his diet after comparing the diets of the average Westerner and his African counterpart. Using everyday British foods Dodson has tried to construct a diet that has some of the same elements as the Third World diet. It seems to work. These patients are normally prescribed a vast array of drugs, but many of them were able to control their blood pressure with the diet alone. After just one month on the diet, the blood pressure of a significant number of the patients had fallen to normal.

However, we do not have to go to extreme lengths to eat

food which will protect us from disease and help us to maintain an ideal weight. We need to cut down our saturated fat consumption by at least a quarter; we need to eat more fibre; and we need to avoid foods which have no nutritional value, but are high in calories, such as sugar.

There is one further factor in our diets which gives rise to a host of debilitating and sometimes fatal diseases: alcohol. In the body alcohol is absorbed through the small intestine and travels to the liver where it is broken down, or metabolised, by the enzyme alcohol dehydrogenase. During a heavy drinking session this enzyme quickly becomes overworked and alcohol starts to find its way into the bloodstream. It is the level of *blood* alcohol that determines how much damage your body is going to sustain. This level is not so much determined by what you drink but rather the speed at which the alcohol leaves the stomach, a factor that depends how fast you are drinking, and how full your stomach is.

Some one million people in Britain are regularly drinking enough to cause serious damage to their health. Each year thousands of people die from diseases brought on by drinking too much alcohol. Ten million working days are probably lost each year through alcohol-induced absenteeism; half of violent crime is perpetrated by people who have been drinking; a third of drivers killed in car crashes are over the legal limit. The social costs of alcohol abuse in Britain probably amount to over two billion pounds a year.

In Britain the average yearly alcohol intake of someone over 15 is 239 pints of beer, nearly 9 pints of spirits, 25 pints of wine, and 12 pints of cider. Although we still drink less alcohol than other countries, many health experts are concerned that women and teenagers are drinking far more dangerously. The amount of alcohol consumed by women rose by 43 per cent between 1978 and 1985. Teenagers are starting to drink at far earlier ages: a recent report carried out by the Royal College of Physicians found that 30 per cent of 13 year olds drink alcohol every other day and that at least 50 per cent of road accidents involving teenagers can be attributed to alcohol in some way.

Drinking too much alcohol damages your prospects for a long, healthy life in a multitude of ways. Perhaps its best known effect is that it can damage the liver and lead to the fatal liver disease cirrhosis. The risk of developing this condition is directly linked to the amount of alcohol consumed.

Between 1970 and 1985 deaths in Britain from cirrhosis increased by over 80 per cent to around 3,000. Alcohol also plays a part in provoking liver cancer. But alcohol abuse does not confine its effects to the liver. It causes and accelerates the onset of disease throughout the body.

Heavy drinkers have higher blood pressure than light drinkers, upping their chances of a heart attack. A recent Swedish study looked at 2,700 middle-aged men over a 10-year period, and used advanced statistical methods to distinguish the factors affecting their health. The study confirmed the known risk factors associated with heart disease like smoking, high blood pressure and high cholesterol levels. However alcohol abuse emerged as an unexpectedly significant factor.

The researchers at the University of Uppsala and at the Karlstad Central Hospital discovered that half of all the men who died suddenly from heart attacks during this period were registered alcoholics. The risk of dying from a heart attack appears to be as much as four times greater for alcoholics than among the population generally. The Swedish researchers have proposed that large amounts of alcohol can cause chemical imbalances which can fatally disturb the heart's rhythm.

The heart is not the only part of the body that alcohol can damage. For a long time doctors have suspected that large quantities of alcohol damage and kill the nerve cells in the brain. This might help to explain why heavy drinking often affects people's memory and concentration, and sometimes provokes aggressive, irrational behaviour.

Researchers in Australia have now confirmed this suspicion by examining human brains during post-mortem examinations. When alcoholics were compared to non-alcoholics it was found that alcoholics had fewer neurones in a part of the brain associated with higher thought processes. The Australian researchers have tentative evidence for two different types of brain damage caused by alcohol. The first of these, which involves the death of brain cells, is irreversible. However there is evidence of a reversible form of brain damage in younger drinkers, offering the hope that if excessive drinking is stopped in time then the brain might be able to recover.

Alcohol has also been linked to cancer of the mouth, throat and oesophagus, gastrointestinal complaints, muscle disorders, degeneration of the central nervous system, lung disease, blood disorders, and increased susceptibility to infection. Prolonged heavy drinking reduces the body's ability to absorb certain foods through the gut and can in severe cases lead to malnutrition and vitamin deficiency. Low income and a poor diet contribute to this malnutrition but a British study of middle-aged, middle-class heavy drinkers showed that nearly a third were malnourished. This malnutrition contributes to the other diseases produced by alcohol excess.

To cap all this, alcohol stops you looking youthful. Too much drink leads to premature ageing of the skin, in particular wrinkling and puffy eyes. In women it can also lead to thinning or loss of hair.

The picture for women is particularly gloomy. Alcohol distributes itself throughout the fluid in the body. This fluid makes up 55 to 65 per cent of the weight of men, but only 45 to 55 per cent of the weight of women. When this is coupled with the smaller physique of a woman, it is easy to see that the concentration of alcohol in a woman will always be greater than in a man who is drinking the same amount. The damage the alcohol causes to the woman's body will thus be greater – especially as her smaller liver is having to cope with this higher concentration.

According to recent studies women who drink even moderate amounts of alcohol may also double their risk of breast cancer. In one study some 7,000 women aged between 25 and 74 were monitored over a 10-year period, at the end of which 121 members of the group had developed breast cancer. The research team discovered that women who consumed just three drinks a week increased their chances of developing breast cancer by 40 to 50 per cent, while women who had one drink or more a day doubled their risk.

Of course, women who drink alcohol may be at risk of breast cancer for all sorts of other reasons, but what cannot be ignored is the fact that a link between alcohol and breast cancer has been found in almost every study that has been carried out. The women most likely to be at risk from the possibility of alcohol-induced breast cancer are those who are obese; those who have had few children; those who had their first child after the age of 25; and those whose mothers suffered from breast cancer.

It is now accepted that a regular daily consumption of over 80 grams of alcohol for men and 40 grams for women constitutes a serious health risk – a half a bottle of wine contains about 32 grams of alcohol. These figures are not cast iron because serious effects on blood pressure in middle-aged men may happen at levels as low as 10 to 25 grams per day, while in pregnant women 10 to 20 grams per day increases the risk of producing a baby of smaller than average size. If a pregnant woman indulges in very heavy drinking the baby may be affected by what is known as the foetal alcohol syndrome, giving the baby characteristic facial abnormalities.

In spite of all this alarming evidence some studies have suggested that a little of what you fancy does you good and that moderate drinkers on average have slightly better health than non-drinkers, living about two years longer. One study was carried out in the UK at Bristol Royal Infirmary. Scientists asked 12 volunteers who were normally light drinkers to drink half a bottle of wine every day for six weeks, and then to abstain for the next six weeks. They found that at the end of the first six weeks, the levels of high-density lipoproteins that sweep cholesterol away to the liver had risen by about 20 per cent. Since increased levels of HDLs are linked to lowered risk of coronary heart disease it does seem that moderate amounts of alcohol can help to protect against heart disease. At the end of the second alcohol-free period, the blood HDL levels of the volunteers had fallen back to normal. The exact mechanism by which alcohol increases the level of HDLs is not really known, although one hypothesis is that it might stimulate the enzymes which manufacture HDLs.

The results were even more startling when cholesterol levels rather than HDLs were measured. People with raised levels of cholesterol in their bile (the green liquid released by the liver) are susceptible to gallstones, solid lumps which block the bile duct causing great pain. The doctors found that at the end of the six 'wet' weeks, bile cholesterol levels in the volunteers fell by nearly a quarter, enough to make the formation of gallstones far less likely. In fact, if everyone at risk drank half a bottle of wine a day, the incidence of gallstones would fall by 60 per cent! Alcohol seems to have an effect on the enzymes that break down excess cholesterol into harmless compounds in the bile.

It has to be stressed that these results were produced with very moderate levels of alcohol consumption. Even half a bottle of wine is more than is needed to reduce the risk of coronaries and gallstones – a quarter bottle is probably enough. However the risks of alcohol consumption are always likely to outweigh the benefits. Recent work, for example, suggests that even moderate drinkers are increasing their chance of a stroke.

Strokes, which kill or disable so many old people, involve the blood supply to part of the brain being cut off because of a blood clot or a burst blood vessel. If the resulting damage is not fatal it often leads to paralysis or loss of speech. The results of a 12-year study in Hawaii showed that drinkers who consumed more than half a bottle of wine a day had nearly three times the chance of suffering a stroke caused by a burst blood vessel compared with a teetotaller. Even light drinkers who consume just one glass of wine a day, or the equivalent in beer and spirits, double their chances of a brain haemorrhage. Although this particular type of stroke is the less common, it is more likely to be fatal.

This research is bad news for the moderate drinker. Until now he could console himself with the knowledge that small amounts of alcohol would protect against heart disease. It now seems that this protection has to be weighed against the increased risks of brain haemorrhage.

Some people are more likely to become alcoholics than others, because hereditary factors are overwhelmingly responsible for this condition. This does not mean that some people are doomed to alcoholism. Instead it means that people at risk can take steps to preserve their health in just the same way as people who inherit a predisposition for coronary disease.

The easiest way to tell if you are at risk is to look back into your family history. If one of your parents or grandparents has suffered from alcoholism, you are also at high risk and should try to modify your drinking. A recent American study found that among a group of 202 alcoholic men, 38 per cent had alcoholic fathers and 21 per cent alcoholic mothers, 57 per cent had alcoholic brothers and 15 per cent had alcoholic sisters, 32 per cent had alcoholic sons, and 19 per cent had alcoholic daughters. The study concluded that by the age of 40 more than half of the men and women with one alcoholic parent will have developed the condition, while among those with two alcoholic parents, around 60 per cent will have it. This compares with the figures for the general American population which show that alcoholism develops in eight to ten per cent of men and three per cent of women.

It does seem that hereditary factors rather than family drinking habits are responsible for the high risk for the children and grandchildren of alcoholics. A Swedish study of adopted children found that the children of alcoholics are four times more likely to become alcoholics, even when adopted early in life.

The key to this genetic link could lie with a pair of enzymes which are involved in the way alcohol is metabolised in the liver. The first of these enzymes, alcohol dehydrogenase, converts alcohol into acetaldehyde, while the second, acetaldehyde dehydrogenase, converts the acetaldehyde into acetic acid.

Acetic acid − better known as vinegar − is easily dealt with by the body. But it is possible that at least some alcoholics inherit a genetic blueprint which leaves them with a slight deficiency of acetaldehyde dehydrogenase, so that they experience difficulty in breaking down all the acetaldehyde that is produced after they have had a drink. Some scientists believe that when this acetaldehyde travels to the brain it produces morphine-like substances which lead to addiction.

According to this hypothesis, which is still contentious, if you inherit a *pronounced* deficiency in acetaldehyde dehydrogenase you are unlikely to become an alcoholic. Even small amounts of drink will then produce high levels of acetaldehyde, bringing on symptoms such as nausea. Perhaps more than 50 per cent of Koreans and Chinese are deficient in this way, and the result is that many people do not drink because they find the experience unpleasant.

It is difficult to recommend safe levels of drinking because of the huge variations in the way individuals respond to alcohol. However the Health Education Authority have suggested some guidelines. They measure alcohol in terms of units, where a unit is the amount of alcohol contained in a half-pint of beer (which is the same amount of alcohol as in a glass of wine, or a pub measure of spirits).

The Authority reckons that to be safe, a man should drink no more than 20 units a week, and a woman 13 units. It does not matter where the units come from: the alcohol in wine has the same effect as alcohol in whisky. If you find that, as a man, you are drinking more than 51 units a week, or as a woman more than 36 units a week, you are likely to start giving yourself serious health problems.

CHAPTER EIGHT

Lifestyles: Running the Body

The idea that exercise can be good for you is not new. As far back as the second century, Galen proclaimed the positive effects of physical training. But whatever present-day fitness enthusiasts might claim, there has been no scientific evidence which conclusively proves that exercise can increase maximum lifespan.

What exercise can do is help us to live long enough to enjoy our average life expectancy – whatever age that is – by slowing down, or in some cases preventing, the physiological decline that so often affects the body as we get older; like, for example, weakening of the bones, loss of muscle tissue and a fall in efficiency of the heart and lungs. Exercise may also help to reduce very high blood pressure, control blood sugar and body weight and lessen the risk of heart attack. There have even been suggestions that certain types of exercise can promote a sense of healthy optimism and help keep that dark companion of ageing – depression – at bay. After all, in terms of evolution, our bodies were designed for a busy, active life in the jungle – not a sedentary existence in front of the television or the word processor.

One of the earliest clues that exercise might help us live longer by protecting us from heart disease was found on a London double decker bus. In 1953 Professor Jerry Morris at the London School of Hygiene and Tropical Medicine compared the rate of heart attack between bus conductors and bus drivers. The difference in terms of the amount of exercise the two engage in every day is obvious. The conductor is constantly on the move as he walks up and down the aisles and climbs the stairs to collect the fares. Over an average eight-hour day, this amount of physical activity is equivalent to climbing the stairs of a 60-storey skyscraper twice a day. Bus drivers, on the other hand, sit down all day; the only exercise they get in the course of their job is changing gear and turning the steering wheel.

By enlisting the help of London Transport, Morris studied the two and discovered that the more active bus conductors had half as many fatal and non-fatal heart attacks as the bus drivers. As far as some scientists were concerned, these results were too good to be true; they argued that people who were already fit would be attracted to the job of bus conductor, while those who tended to shy away from regular exercise would prefer to sit down all day and drive the bus, rather than run around collecting fares.

Morris found the answer to his critics when, 20 years after his original – and much quoted – observations, he published the results of another survey in the 1973 edition of the British journal *The Lancet*. This drew on the results of a questionnaire Morris had given to 17,000 middle-aged male civil servants, all with sedentary jobs, asking them to describe the way they spent their leisure time on a Friday and Saturday. After three years Morris analysed his data and discovered that those men who spent Friday and Saturday doing some sort of 'vigorous' exercise, like digging the garden or swimming, had half the risk of experiencing a heart attack as those whose only exercise was getting out of bed every morning. The use of the description 'vigorous' is very important because Morris discovered that the exercise had to reach a certain intensity before it had any beneficial effect on the heart. This threshold level of exercise was described in terms of energy expenditure which is measured in units called kilocalories and averaged out at a figure of 7.5 kilocalories every minute. The sorts of exercise that come into this category are jogging, cycling, swimming, tennis and running.

A follow-up study was carried out in 1980, and Morris reconfirmed his earlier findings that it was the men who had spent time engaging in bursts of vigorous activity of one sort or another who suffered fewest heart attacks. These results were startling; this was the first time anyone had suggested the total amount of exercise was not as important as bursts of high-intensity, vigorous exercise.

Meanwhile, Professor Ralph Paffenbarger at Stanford University in California was undertaking a study of American workers that was to confirm Morris's findings. He decided to look at the incidence of heart attacks among men who would normally expend vast amounts of energy during their daily work and settled for labourers in the San Francisco docks. Those dockers who routinely used bursts of energy in the region of between 5.2 and 7.5 kilocalories per minute had half the risk of heart attack of those dockers who had a lower output of between 2.4 and 5.9 kilocalories per minute.

Paffenbarger went on to compare his high-energy dock workers with more relaxed and less active ageing university graduates. Just like Morris, he sent out questionnaires to thousands of men – this time graduates aged between 35 and 74 – and asked them to describe the amount of energy they used up by detailing the frequency of various types of activities like climbing stairs, walking and organised sport. Surprisingly, he discovered that those graduates who climbed 50 steps a day or walked distances or more than half a mile had a quarter of the risk of heart attack of those who were less active. Graduates who were even more active and expended about 2,000 kilocals a week reduced their risk of heart attack by as much as 40 per cent.

The benefits gained from vigorous activity were the same for all the Harvard graduates and the London civil servants regardless of their age. Men who undertake vigorous exercise of whatever sort are protected from heart attacks despite their weight, smoking habits, blood pressure levels or history of heart disease in the family. To achieve this sort of protection, the exercise has to be vigorous enough to have a significant effect on the heart and the muscles. As we discovered in the last chapter, the heart gets its supply of oxygen from blood travelling from the lungs through the coronary arteries. If any of those arteries are blocked with fatty plugs then the blood supply will be restricted and the amount of oxygen available to the heart and muscles will be severely reduced. More importantly, the risk of heart attack rises dramatically. The amount of oxygen that the heart needs to function properly is affected by two factors: heart rate and blood pressure. So the way to protect the heart from a potential heart attack is either by reducing heart rate or by reducing blood pressure. This would mean that if the arteries were already narrowing, reducing the heart rate or blood pressure allows the oxygen demand to match oxygen supply. Exercise is able to do this by reducing the heart rate; it is known as the 'training effect'. This positive effect of exercise is so pronounced that it is not unusual for trained athletes to have resting heart rates as low as 38 beats a minute compared to the usual 72 beats a minute. If the athlete's heart can pump as efficiently using only 38 beats compared to 72, then more blood must be being expelled at every contraction; this is called the 'stroke volume'.

Athletes who train regularly will also speed up their 'venous return', which is the time it takes to push the blood through the veins and back to the heart. This combination of a slower heart rate, quicker venous return and increased stroke volume encourages the heart to stretch, and expand more as it fills, giving more power on each contraction.

As well as changes to the heart, exercise also produces improvements in the muscles. After periods of vigorous exercise they are able to extract more oxygen from the blood, and the number of capillaries that supply the muscle also increases, allowing more oxygenated blood to reach the exercising muscle. This means that even at a slower heart rate there is still enough oxygenated blood getting to the muscles so the heart has to do less work. So the idea is not to train the heart, but to train the muscles to reduce the amount of work the heart has to do.

Paffenbarger's study even came up with the tentative suggestion that vigorous exercise had an effect – albeit small – on life expectancy. This works out at about an extra two years in which to relax or generally enjoy your new-found fitness. A long-term Finnish study tested this theory by relating the effect of different types of exercise on mortality rate. The participants were many and varied and included office workers, shop keepers, farmers and lumberjacks; these in turn were assigned to a category depending on whether their jobs consisted of light, moderate or heavy physical activity. To calculate their overall level of activity sporting habits were also taken into account – so, physical activity was labelled as high if

a person's occupation demanded heavy labour and their hob-
bies included walking, cycling or cross-country skiing.

Like the Harvard graduates, those Finns in the high-activity
group increased their average life expectancy by about two
years mainly due to a reduced risk of coronary heart disease.
Sadly this study produced no evidence that exercise could
extend maximum lifespan since any life-extending benefits had
disappeared by the age of 85.

Paffenbarger's study also showed that these sort of positive
effects cannot be stored: graduates who had once been physically active and then given up had no reduction in their rate of
heart attacks. Former college athletes only retained their low
risk of heart attack if they carried on exercising into middle age.
Athletes who had failed to do this and turned their backs on
physical exercise were worse off than those who took up sport
in middle age. The moral of the exercise story seems to be that
the benefits of youthful exercise cannot be saved up to protect
the heart against the excesses of middle age, but it can be
worthwhile developing an interest in exercise long after the
hair has started to thin and the wrinkles have appeared.

More good news for the less than enthusiastic fitness devotee
is the finding that as well as a lower limit of exercise below
which the health benefits are not obvious, there is also an upper
limit beyond which no further protective effect on the heart is
seen. This upper limit seems to be around 2,000 to 2,500
kilocalories per week (equivalent to 20 miles of jogging a week)
and means that it isn't necessary to jog, or flog, yourself into
the ground in order to reduce the risk of heart attack;
apparently running 100 miles a week is no better than running a
mere 20, although for some people even clocking up 20 miles
will be a struggle.

Obviously none of these surveys carried out on people are
perfect; this sort of scientific field known as epidemiology is
fraught with problems since the human being is a complex
subject to study, but it seems fair to interpret these and
subsequent results as giving weight to the idea that vigorous
exercise reduces the risk of heart attack. To try to work out the
way in which exercise could protect the heart, and help us live
longer, scientists in San Diego turned their scientific gaze on to

an animal not renowned for its interest in the sporting life – the pig.

According to some exercise physiologists pigs and humans have more in common than meets the eye. Not only do pigs have a very similar way of breaking down their food to release energy, they also have similar eating patterns but, more importantly, their hearts are also very similar: a single blocked coronary artery in either species can cause enough damage to lead to a fatal heart attack. Pigs also share our aversion to exercise: it's not common to see a pig jogging around the farmyard.

In 1980 this encouraged Dr Colin Bloor and his colleagues in California to design an exercise experiment in which 10 little pigs went jogging, while another 10 stayed at home – or at least in the laboratory. The early results were disappointing. After jogging up to 25 miles a week for periods as long as twelve months, the exercising pigs may have been fitter, but they certainly weren't living longer than the pigs who had rested their trotters and adopted the porcine version of the good life. In spite of painstaking analysis of samples of their blood and exhaled breath there were no clues to link exercise and longevity. The only positive result was that all the exercising pigs lost weight even though they were given unlimited quantities of food.

Still, the jogging pigs were only really able to bask in the academic limelight when the researchers changed their experiment. What would happen, they wondered, if pigs with already diseased hearts were used for comparison? To mimic the sort of damage seen during heart disease, a balloon was placed around one of the three main arteries leading to each pig's heart. When expanded the balloon squeezed the artery, restricting the flow of blood so that after a short time parts of the heart muscle died and the pigs developed heart disease. Once again half the pigs were given no exercise, while the others put on their running shoes. All the pigs developed new pathways that bypassed the damaged area and allowed blood to reach their hearts, but the number and size of the arteries and the amount of blood going through them increased in the jogging pigs far more than in the non-joggers. This suggests that exercise is a benefit to a pig whose heart is already threatened by coronary artery disease. Clearly it would not be easy to repeat these experiments with humans, but some scientists believe that exercise could benefit those people who have already had a heart attack.

Doctors used to prescribe long periods of rest after a heart attack, but now patients are encouraged to undertake gentle forms of exercise. Even if this exercise does not cause new pathways for the blood to travel through the heart muscle, it can still help by cutting down the amount of oxygen the heart needs so that the patients can carry out more physical activities before they suffer chest pain. The rehabilitation programme often includes exercises to increase flexibility and muscle strength, along with simple activities like shaving, washing and feeding.

In Toronto a cardiac rehabilitation centre offers heart attack patients a carefully supervised exercise programme in which they progress from gentle walking to jogging – and eventually, in some cases, to marathons! After 10 years and 700 patients the research team found that the rate of death from a sub-sequent heart attack dropped to 20 per cent of what was once regarded as normal. Rehabilitation centres for cardiac patients in the UK are not very common but one that comes recom-mended by exercise specialists is based at Preston in Lancashire.

Here coronary patients are put on to the exercise pro-gramme the day after they come into hospital. The exercises are tailor-made for the individual but are carefully supervised for the whole of the two-week stay in the cardiac unit. Three weeks after the attack patients return to hospital for an exercise stress test which is used to test the health of the heart under the strain of exercise – usually while jogging on a treadmill.

The third and final stage of the exercise programme lasts for about 12 months and consists of exercise workouts on three evenings a week after the patient has been discharged from hospital. It's a bit too soon to draw firm conclusions, but it does seem that the overall death rate and incidence of further heart attacks is lower for the Preston patients than coronary patients who don't exercise.

Exercise is even being recommended for patients with high blood pressure. In Australia patients with high blood pressure were prescribed three different types of physical activity, inactive, mild and moderate, for three successive months. The results were predictable: mild exercise significantly reduced blood pressure while moderate exercise had an even greater effect. The reductions in blood pressure achieved by exercising are important because they could help to avoid the use of drug treatment – unlike exercise, drugs are expensive and can have unpleasant side-effects.

While most people know they should take more exercise, what they do not realize is just how easily they may be taking the wrong sort of exercise and giving themselves more problems that they started with. In the UK, scientists at Loughborough University calculate how much someone is benefiting from exercise and they draw a very clear distinction between two different sorts of exercise. Professor Clyde Williams and his colleagues analyse breath and blood samples to measure whether exercise is aerobic or anaerobic. Exercise always starts off 'aerobically', which literally means 'depending on oxygen', and the body uses this oxygen to burn fat and carbohydrate stored in our bodies to release energy and fuel the muscles as fast as possible.

The body switches from aerobic to anaerobic release of energy when the level of exercise becomes so intense that the energy released by the aerobic metabolism of fat and carbohydrate isn't enough to keep up with the demands of the muscles. During anaerobic exercise the body releases energy by a rapid breakdown of the limited stores of a sugar called glycogen in the muscles. In the process lactic acid is produced which builds up and eventually inhibits the further breakdown of glycogen producing the energy crisis we call fatigue, often with the characteristic pain we experience during an attack of cramp. All of which means that when it comes to keeping fit, choosing the right form of exercise is vitally important. If all you do is to perform in sudden bursts, putting enormous demands on your muscles (as in squash for example), then there will be no aerobic benefits. Anaerobic exercise tends to produce higher blood pressure and, since the amount of oxygen needed by the heart is related to blood pressure, more oxygen will be required during a game like squash. If the coronary arteries supplying the heart with oxygenated blood are normal then these oxygen needs can easily be satisfied. If however the arteries are already beginning to build up fatty deposits, then it will be harder for the blood to get through, blood pressure will rise and the risk of heart attack increases. Many cases of sudden death and heart attack are thought to occur as a result of playing squash, either during or shortly after the game. In order to get aerobically fit enough to play a game like squash without putting undue strain on the body, longer, less demanding, *aerobic* forms of exercise, such as cycling, swimming or jogging, are needed.

It is all right for fully fit athletes to develop their strength and build up their bodies with the more anaerobic forms of exercise, but for those of us with only health and a longer life as our aim, anaerobic exercise will not benefit the heart or lead to fitness: aerobic exercise is what is needed.

Most exercise physiologists recommend that in order for exercise to be aerobic and reduce the risk of heart disease, three or four sessions a week that last for 20–30 minutes are necessary; three weekly sessions of 20 minutes will have more of an effect than one 60-minute thrash. Each session has to be vigorous enough to increase heart rate to about 75 per cent of what is called the heart rate reserve. First you need to find out your maximum heart rate which as a rule of thumb should be roughly equivalent to 220 beats a minute minus your age. So if you are 30 years old, the maximum heart rate will be 220 minus 30 which is 190. The heart reserve is the difference between this figure and the normal heart rate. The simplest way to work out normal heart rate is to press a finger on to the wrist and count the beats of the pulse for 10 seconds. Multiply this number by 6 to give the pulse rate per minute. Subtract this from the maximum heart rate to give the heart rate reserve; for example if the resting heart rate is 70, then the heart rate reserve is 190 minus 70 which is 120. You don't really have to be a mathematics professor to work out that 75 per cent of your heart rate reserve will be 90. Add back on the resting heart rate of 70 and 160 is the target you should aim for during aerobic exercise. Taking your pulse as you exercise will tell you whether or not you have achieved this; in other words your ideal pulse rate for 10 seconds should be 26 to 27 beats. If your pulse rate rises above this number then the exercise is too extreme, and you should slow down: if the number is lower than the ideal for your age you can safely increase the pace.

A rough rule of thumb is that aerobic exercise should be strenuous enough to make you feel out of breath, but not so extreme that you can't catch your breath to carry on a normal conversation while exercising. It is never meant to feel uncomfortable or to cause pain or tightness across any part of the upper body like the chest, arms, throat or jaw. If any of these symptoms do occur then you should stop exercising immediately and see your doctor. If you are very unfit, it will be dangerous to attempt three 20-minute sessions; start exercising at a very relaxed pace and build up intensity and duration gradually.

The protective effect of exercise on the heart is also thought to be due to the changes it produces in the types of fats circulating in the blood. Exercise seems to increase the level of an enzyme that breaks down fat stored in the form of triglycerides. This leads to the manufacture of more fat-carrying particles called high-density lipoproteins (HDLs). As we discovered in Chapter Seven, high-density lipoproteins carry cholesterol from the tissues to the liver. It has been suggested that aerobic exercise has a beneficial effect on the heart by increasing the levels of HDLs in the blood so that cholesterol is carried away from the coronary arteries faster than it can be deposited. This would reduce the chances of a heart attack caused by blocked arteries.

Just as Morris discovered that the benefits of vigorous exercise only occurred at certain levels, a research team at Stanford University in California discovered that exercise has to reach a certain intensity before it will raise levels of HDLs in the blood. When the American team put male university employees on to a 12-month programme of exercise they discovered that they had to run for at least 12 to 15 miles every week before any obvious increases of HDLs were measured in their blood.

This finding seemed to be confirmed when the HDL level in blood taken from lumberjacks was compared to that of the more sedentary electrician. Predictably, the more active lumberjacks had higher levels of HDLs. Other experiments have suggested that the type of exercise is also important; sprinters and icehockey players have lower levels of HDLs than long-distance runners. This isn't as dire as it first sounds; it has now been proved that a respectable increase in HDL levels can be produced by the amounts of exercise most of us would consider within our reach. These reassuring results came from a study in which unfit men were tested before and after an exercise regime which included running, jogging or walking five to six miles every week. After two months on the pro-gramme, HDL levels had increased by 50 per cent. Like the studies carried out by Morris and Paffenbarger this work is not without its critics because again it is not clear cut in a scientific sense, since as we discovered in the last chapter, a diet rich in saturated or unsaturated fat can also have a powerful influence on the circulating levels of HDLs. This complex interaction between diet and exercise was highlighted by another study involving lumberjacks – this time in Finland. Finland has one of the highest rates of heart disease in the world and Finnish scientists discovered that even though the lumberjacks were expending levels of energy equivalent to running 50 to 100 miles a week, they succumbed to heart disease more often than sedentary workers.

One explanation for this contradictory result might lie in the composition of the lumberjack's diet. As might be expected, lumberjacks have very healthy appetites and consume up to two to three times the amount of food eaten by their less active work mates. Increasing their food intake in this way could do more than satisfy a big appetite, because the Finns, like the British, have a diet based on meat and dairy products which means they eat large quantities of saturated fat. The lum-berjacks might be consuming so much fat that cholesterol will be deposited in the coronary arteries despite the beneficial effects of vigorous physical activity. So, eating a sensible diet will obviously increase the benefits of exercise on the body.

Studies of people from all walks of life – policemen, students, firemen and hospital patients – have revealed they all feel more positive about their lives even after a small amount of exercise which is often not vigorous enough to have any effect on the heart and muscles. This sort of psychological benefit of exercise can be put down to common sense; organised exercise can bring people together in groups, and in doing so can give people more confidence in building relationships at the same time as giving them more control over their bodies; it can also increase stamina and allow people to engage in more activities without tiring. However, there is now research which suggests that these effects of exercise may be due to changes in our brain chemistry.

At Loma Linda University in California scientists measure the way in which exercise produces chemicals called endorphins. Since endorphins have been found to have a similar chemical structure to morphine, they have been dubbed the body's natural pain killers. Researchers cannot agree whether endorphins are responsible for the extreme sense of euphoria described in the popular press as the 'runner's high', but they may account for the intense feeling of addiction that some enthusiasts – particularly marathon and long-distance runners – claim for their sport. Whether or not the mental benefits of exercise can be explained in terms of endorphins, the sense of well-being is a good incentive to take up exercise and often an adequate reward for those who already exercise.

The benefits to be gained from aerobic exercise not only include effects on the heart and the brain; it is also thought that regular activity can slow down the sort of physiological deterioration that is a part of normal ageing. As we age we replace muscle with fat; the average person is thought to lose half a pound of lean tissue and gain a pound of fat every year between the age of 35 and 65. By increasing the energy expenditure of the body, exercise can limit this increase in body fat while at the same time it can help to build muscle when it is normally lost.

As for the ageing athlete, it is still possible to be fit if, like some of those Harvard graduates, he remains physically active. In the USA Michael Pollock has carried out a longitudinal study of athletes that has been continuing since the 1970s. Most of his subjects have been a group of athletes aged between 50 and 82, many of them of former world-class standard.

His results have shed a very optimistic light on the effects of exercise on the body, since many of the changes once thought to be inevitable are now known not to be so. Heart rate was thought to decline steadily throughout our adult lives, along with maximum oxygen uptake. Many of the athletes in Pollock's group were able to maintain their oxygen uptake at youthful levels while some were even able to increase it as they got older. This refusal of the athletes' bodies to exhibit the expected declines of old age has led to the idea that physically active people have bodies which function very much like those of younger people.

Another direct effect on the ageing process is that exercise can slow down, or even reverse, the onset of the crippling bone disease osteoporosis. This is a disease in which calcium is lost from the bones making them brittle and more likely to break under any stress or trauma like a fall. In the USA, osteoporosis accounts for more than one million fractures a year: American researchers have discovered that by the age of 65 one-third of women will have fractures of the vertebrae while by the age of 81 one-third of women and one-sixth of men will have suffered a fractured hip – which will often end in death. Both men and women start to lose bone as early as their twenties and thirties, but in women this bone loss accelerates rapidly after the menopause.

Bone, like any other tissue in the body, is dynamic – it constantly renews itself. Depending on what is happening inside the body, bone will either need to be formed or to be broken down. These changes are brought about by the action of two different types of bone cells called osteoblasts and osteoclasts: the two work together as a construction team and demolition team using calcium as their building material. Normally these two processes are balanced and work together to ensure that the body's needs are met. The problem comes with old age when the osteoblasts become less active and the balance moves towards demolition rather than construction. As a result the bones become thinner and much more fragile. Exercise can help because it somehow restores the natural balance, possibly by putting mechanical stress on the bone and triggering the construction team to go into action.

As well as being interesting in theory, this process also seems to work in practice; when a group of elderly American women were asked to exercise for half an hour three times a day, over a period of three years, their bones remained strong and healthy, while a similar group who had no exercise suffered from breaks and fractures.

Exercise is also proving effective in helping to control diabetes. Diabetes occurs when the levels of sugar in the blood rise steeply due to a deficiency of the hormone insulin; normally insulin is used by the body to mop up any excess sugar that isn't being used to release energy. During aerobic exercise the muscles use sugar to produce energy so an exercising diabetic should not have to rely on so many insulin injections.

Physical activity may also have an important role to play in another form of diabetes called type 11 or non-insulin dependent diabetes. As its name suggests, this form of the disease is not caused by a lack of the hormone insulin, but rather by lack of sensitivity of the cells to it. As the cells cease to respond to the hormone, uptake of sugar falls off and levels in the blood become dangerously high. Evidence to support this theory is not yet conclusive, but experiments with rats which were encouraged to run on treadmills suggest that exercise can improve the sensitivity of the cells to insulin and so help to balance out the sugar in the blood. This may also be because exercise causes the release of two other hormones; adrenaline and noradrenaline. During exercise levels of both of these hormones rise and both also cause insulin levels to fall. The resulting fall in insulin and the fact that excess sugar in the blood will be used up by the exercising muscles should help to even out blood sugar levels naturally.

Before we get too carried away with the benefits of exercise there is some scientific evidence to suggest that everything in the health clubs is not always rosy. Extreme exercise has been known to lead to infertility in women and fatal heart attacks in men.

For millions of Americans addicted to the joys of pounding the sidewalk, the summer of 1984 was not a happy one. On Friday 20 July, James Fixx, fitness guru and author of the best-selling *The Complete Book of Running*, went out for his usual run along the back roads of Vermont, and died shortly afterwards. At the age of 52, heart disease had almost completely blocked two of his coronary arteries. For those who had followed in Fixx's footsteps and taken up their running shoes, the irony was obvious. If exercise was so good for you why did it not protect Jim Fixx? His death was taken up as a *cause célèbre* by the media, who used it as an opportunity to voice similar doubts and questions about the benefits of exercise. From a scientific point of view most of the answers could be found by taking a closer look at Jim Fixx's lifestyle.

Before his conversion into a born-again athlete, Jim Fixx had been overweight and smoked two packets of cigarettes a day. After his father died from a heart attack at the age of 43, he apparently reassessed his habits and changed his lifestyle. With such a history of heart disease it is possible that running had actually prolonged his life and if he had carried on indulging in his former unhealthy habits then he might have died much sooner. According to the pathologist in Vermont, Fixx's arteries were so severely clogged up with fatty deposits his chances of dying that day were high, even if he had not been running.

With such an advanced case of heart disease, many doctors were puzzled that Fixx had experienced no symptoms up until his death. Friends and colleagues later admitted that Fixx had complained of warning signs like pain in the throat and jaw, but had chosen to ignore them. He had also refused to take an exercise stress test which would have identified his heart problems and almost certainly saved his life.

For people like Fixx who have inherited heart disease, many doctors now believe that the progression of the disease can only be halted in a very minor way, if at all, by exercise. In those prone to the disease, fatty deposits can be laid down in the coronary arteries by the age of 20, and this process will often be speeded up – as perhaps happened with Jim Fixx – by abusing the body with alcohol, tobacco, and a diet high in saturated fats. As with the lumberjacks in Finland, vigorous exercise is capable of increasing the formation of large numbers of protective HDLs, but it cannot keep up with the accumulation of large quantities of fatty deposits. Once the major arteries to the heart are blocked with fat, any extra effort – especially physical activity like jogging or running – will put too great a load on the heart and a heart attack can result.

To be on the safe side it is often suggested that anyone over the age of 40 who has been aware of warning symptoms like tightness in the throat, a crushing sensation in the chest or any severe pain in the upper arms should consult a doctor before taking up vigorous exercise. The patient may be sent for an exercise stress test to try and determine if there is any underlying heart disease. The test is really a more sophisticated version of an electrocardiogram (ECG) which is administered during exercise to try to identify any part of the heart where oxygen supplies might be abnormally low indicating a blocked artery. It has been estimated that about 80 per cent of people with coronary artery disease can be screened using this test so that doctors can then work out how much exercise would be safe. However, these tests are not easy to administer and, in the UK, at the moment are not really considered cost effective enough to be offered on the National Health Service.

For anyone who does not have a family history of heart disease, has never experienced symptoms of heart diseases and is not overweight, the risks of dying of a heart attack during exercise are so small as to be insignificant. Studies into the deaths of joggers show that death during exercise is extremely rare. In Rhode Island in the USA, American researchers estimated that over the five-year period from 1975 to 1980, there was one death for 7,620 joggers. Likewise in Finland, of 2,606 sudden deaths only 22 were linked to sports – 16 with skiing, two with jogging and four with other activities.

These figures underline the fact that the risks of dying from exercise are negligible compared to the risks of not exercising, since as we discovered earlier, those who do not exercise regularly are more than twice as likely to suffer a heart attack as those who do.

For those people who are reluctant to get out of their armchairs, the good news is that to have a positive effect on health exercise doesn't have to involve as much pain as they imagine. All that's needed is a period of activity that will fit easily into one's life; as long as it increases the pulse rate to 75 per cent of the maximum heart rate it will have an effect. For the very unfit, it may be better to build up the level of physical activity very slowly perhaps by making small changes in lifestyle, like climbing the stairs rather than taking the lift, treating the dog to a brisk workout across the neighbourhood or even parking the car further away from the office. As long as you exert yourself enough to feel out of breath then the heart and lungs will benefit. Once your level of fitness has improved you can go on to other activities like jogging, swimming or other sports if you wish.

Whether or not exercise can increase maximum lifespan, it will certainly keep us healthy and allow us to enjoy life for a longer period of time by staving off the diseases of old age. With a combination of exercise and diet, we can achieve our goal of living out our lifespan and experiencing a healthy old age.

Conclusion

'I don't want to achieve immortality through my work, I want to achieve it through not dying.'

Woody Allen

The ageing process and the diseases associated with it are not immutable. In principle, and increasingly in practice, they can be controlled in just the same way as we control the onset of other conditions in the body.

Of course, it might seem that tampering with the ageing process will cause more problems than it solves, but with the number of older people in society growing rapidly, health and social services will soon be swamped unless steps are taken to prevent the decline in health that comes with old age. At the moment gerontology is primarily concerned with finding ways to allow us to live out three-score years and ten in good health. Altering the maximum possible lifespan is only a secondary aim, and is a prospect that raises terrifying problems. However, we have to accept that if we are to reach our inherited life expectancy without the degeneration of our minds and bodies, scientists must delve into the factors that control the human lifespan.

At the moment there is no test tube containing the Elixir of Youth, labelled 'drink me', although some immortalists continue their quasi-scientific version of *Alice in Wonderland*. Nevertheless, science fiction is being replaced by science fact. If we shape our lives according to the new research we stand a much better chance of reaching our inherited life expectancy without succumbing to disease.

The increase in research effort has meant that it is now possible to distinguish between normal ageing and specific conditions that show themselves as we get older; diseases like arthritis, diabetes, cancer, Parkinson's disease, stroke and Alzheimer's. These are now known to be separate processes set apart from the pattern of normal ageing and in many cases can be cured.

Scientists have even discovered how to manipulate the immune system to extend maximum lifespan – at least in fish and rats! Over the next few years we will all eagerly watch Dr Walford's progress to see if his life-extending diet really does work, and if the results found in mice can be applied to men.

However, in the short term there is plenty we can do to extend our average lifespan. Controlling extreme levels of stress at work or in our personal lives will help preserve our immune system longer; while maintaining an active interest in our work, family and friends well into old age will exercise our minds, prevent mental decline and stave off depression. Taking care to avoid foods that might increase our risk of heart disease and cancer, and accepting that smoking will shorten our lifespan will give us a better chance of reaching old age with all our faculties – and organs – intact, and free from disease.

Being born female is still an advantage – at least in the longevity stakes. By the year 2000 twice as many women in the USA are expected to reach 65 years or older but the flipside of the coin is that ageing women are also prone to more chronic diseases. However long they live, women of all ages must now accept that alcohol poses a serious threat to their health, while osteoporosis remains an unpleasant part of getting older. But this is where a small adjustment in lifestyle can reap enormous benefits, since exercise has been shown to prevent the loss of calcium from ageing bones.

Devoting time to physical activity will pay dividends for all of us: reducing our chances of a heart attack, making it easier to control diabetes and making us feel better about life in general.

None of the proposed changes in lifestyle have to be adopted with evangelical fervour: there are no drums beating or cymbals clashing, just the slow realisation that scientific research has done the groundwork and outlined the hurdles to be overcome on the way to achieving successful ageing. The rest is up to us.

Bibliography

Handbook of the Biology of Aging, Ed. Finch C. E. and Hayflick L., Van Nostrand Reinhold Company, London

The Biology of Senescence, Alex Comfort, Elsevier, New York

How to Live Longer and Feel Better, Linus Pauling, W. H. Freeman & Company, New York

The Healthy Heart Program, Terence Kavanagh, Rodale Press, Pennsylvania

Why Exercise?, David Ashton and Bruce Davies, Basil Blackwell, Oxford

The 120-Year Diet, Roy Walford, Simon & Schuster, New York

Maximum Lifespan, Roy Walford, W. W. Norton & Company, New York

Don't Break Your Heart!, Barry Lynch, Sidgwick & Jackson, London

Ageing, Ioan Davies, Edward Arnold, London

New Life for Old, David Abbott, Frederick Muller Ltd, London

An End to Ageing, Stephen Fulder, Thorson Publishers Ltd, Northamptonshire

The Monkey Gland Affair, David Hamilton, Chatto & Windus, London

Rejuvenation, Norman Haire, George Allen & Unwin Ltd, London

Your Memory, A User's Guide, Alan Baddeley, Sidgwick & Jackson, London

The Biology of Aging, Behnke, Finch and Moment, Plenum Press, New York

Text Book of Geriatric Medicine and Gerontology, Brockelhurst J. C. (Ed.), Churchill Livingstone, London

Tomorrows's World: Food, Caroline Van den Brul and Sue Spindler, BBC Publications, London

Index

220 INDEX

Barnard, Christiaan, 54, 148–49, 151
basal ganglia, 106
Beauvoir, Simone de, 3
Beechams' Research Laboratories, 179
benzoic acid, 62
benzophenones, 133
bereavement, 92, 93, 94
beta carotene, 38, 146
bile, 193, 194
bile acids, 187
Bio-erectile, 57–58
biofeedback, 95
biological age, 19
Black Death, 8
Black Oxen (Atherton), 45
Blank, I.H., 136
blindness, in premature infants, 37, 40
blood circulation rate, 16
blood clot
 see thrombosis
blood disorders, 192
blood pressure, 95, 160, 175–6, 182, 189–90, 193, 199, 200, 204, 205
 high 16, 22, 60, 66, 91–2, 95, 159, 168, 169, 175–6, 180, 181, 182, 191, 197, 204, 205
blood sugar, 197, 210
blood transfusions, 1, 2
Bloor, Dr Colin, 202
BMR (basal metabolic rate), 177
body temperature, 4, 79–84 passim, 123, 127
body weight, and exercise, 197
bone, and exercise, 209–10, 215
bone changes, 16, 197
bovine serum albumen, 142
bowel cancer, 169, 188
brain, and immune system, 90–1, 92
brain changes, 16, 34, 99, 100, 103, 104, 105, 114, 118–19, 121

brain chemistry, 208
brain damage, and alcohol, 191–2
brain-grafting, 53, 110–13, 117, 118
brain haemorrhage, 194
brain tumour, 7, 99
breast cancer, 60, 93, 94, 169, 176, 186, 187, 192, 193
breathing rate, 95
Brinkley, 'Doctor' J. R., 48–49, 51
Bristol Royal Infirmary, 193
British Medical Association, 184
British Medical Journal, 62, 95
bronchitis, 184
Brown, Michael, 172
Brown-Séquard, Charles, 2, 44, 58, 73
brown fat theory, 178–80
Brunel University, 36, 39
burst blood vessel, 194
butanoic acid, 188
butter, 173

calcium, 31, 82, 174, 182, 189, 209, 215
calcium salts, 16
calorie restriction, 61, 73, 74, 75, 76, 77, 178, 180, 186, 190
cancer, 3, 10, 18, 21, 41–2, 66, 67, 72, 74, 79, 85, 88, 89, 93, 94, 96, 97, 143, 149, 150, 164, 166, 176, 182, 184, 187, 215
 see also individual cancers
Cancer Research Institute, Philadelphia, 74
car crash deaths, and alcohol, 190
carbohydrates, 187–8, 189, 204
carbon monoxide, 183–184
cardiac arrest, 168
cardiac rehabilitation centres, 203
cardiovascular disease, 10
 see also heart attack, heart disease
Carrel, Alexis, 20, 21
catalase, 38
cataracts, 18, 22, 79